*Revised Edition*

*Untangled Roots Series: Genealogical Novels Volume 1*

# Thomas the Melungeon:
His Locust Family of Free Persons of Color
Civil and Revolutionary War Patriots

## Gigi Best

BBRT Associates LLC Publishing
Tampa, Florida

*On Cover:* Oil painting of Locust-Fuller Ancestors © Gigi Best

BBRT Associates LLC publishing
3108 North Boundary Blvd.
Building 926-170, Tampa, FL 33621
www.bradlcmuseum.com

**BBRT Associates LLC Publishing**
Editor-in-Chief  *Gigi Best*

**Photo Credits**
Chief Photographer:  *Skip (S.R.) Richardson*
Photo Editing:  *Nate Best*
Ft. Macon State Park
The Lincoln University Class Book 1900

Manufactured in the United States of America
Second Edition: 1ˢᵗ Printing
Revised December 2020

Library of Congress Control Number:  2015931571
ISBN-13:978-0-69237208-1
ISBN-10:0692372083

Dedicated to my daughter, Deneen; grandmother, Rosetta Fuller Best, Cousins Samuel Jackson, Simon Zephaniah Jackson, all founding members of the Jackson Family Reunion Committee originated more than 50 years ago.

To my mother, Izzie Campbell Best Cowdery; great aunt, Daisy Campbell Coley; Aunt Wilhelmina Yelverton Best; and cousins, Ruth Wise and Gloria "Tom" Seenarine, who provided family genealogy, stories, wisdom, and the fortitude to complete this book.

My kind and gentle husband of 35 years, Skip Richardson, for his support and encouragement through extensive hours of study. He assisted me at many research facilities and nourished me.

G.B.

## Three of Thomas Locust Fuller's Sons

*1870-1932*
*Rev. Lemuel H. Fuller, Minister,*
*School Teacher and Principal.*
*Eldest Son of Thomas*
*Graduated Lincoln Univer. 1898*
*Author's Collection.*

*1874-1956*
*Daniel Fuller, Farmer*
*Second Son of Thomas*
*Author's Collection.*

*1881-1973*
*Peter Garfield Fuller,*
*County Agricultural Agent*
*Fourth Son of Thomas*
*Graduated Hampton U. 1913*
*L. Fuller's Collection.*

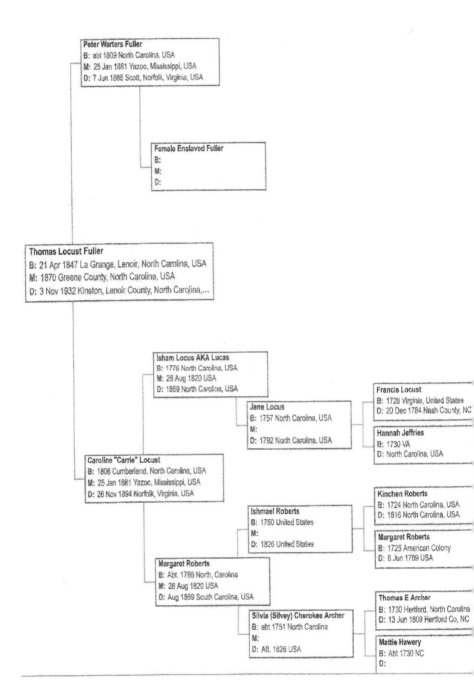

**Peter Warters Fuller**
B: abt 1809 North Carolina, USA
M: 25 Jan 1881 Yazoo, Mississippi, USA
D: 7 Jun 1885 Scott, Norfolk, Virginia, USA

**Female Enslaved Fuller**
B:
M:
D:

**Thomas Locust Fuller**
B: 21 Apr 1847 La Grange, Lenoir, North Carolina, USA
M: 1870 Greene County, North Carolina, USA
D: 3 Nov 1932 Kinston, Lenoir County, North Carolina,...

**Isham Locus AKA Lucas**
B: 1776 North Carolina, USA
M: 26 Aug 1820 USA
D: 1869 North Carolina, USA

**Jane Locus**
B: 1757 North Carolina, USA
M:
D: 1792 North Carolina, USA

**Francis Locust**
B: 1728 Virginia, United States
D: 20 Dec 1784 Nash County, NC

**Hannah Jeffries**
B: 1730 VA
D: North Carolina, USA

**Caroline "Carrie" Locust**
B: 1806 Cumberland, North Carolina, USA
M: 25 Jan 1881 Yazoo, Mississippi, USA
D: 26 Nov 1894 Norfolk, Virginia, USA

**Ishmael Roberts**
B: 1750 United States
M:
D: 1826 United States

**Kinchen Roberts**
B: 1724 North Carolina, USA
D: 1816 North Carolina, USA

**Margaret Roberts**
B: 1725 American Colony
D: 6 Jun 1789 USA

**Margaret Roberts**
B: Abt. 1786 North, Carolina
M: 26 Aug 1820 USA
D: Aug 1869 South Carolina, USA

**Silvia (Silvey) Cherokee Archer**
B: abt 1751 North Carolina
M:
D: Aft. 1826 USA

**Thomas E Archer**
B: 1730 Hertford, North Carolina
D: 13 Jun 1809 Hertford Co, NC

**Mattie Hawery**
B: Abt 1730 NC
D:

4

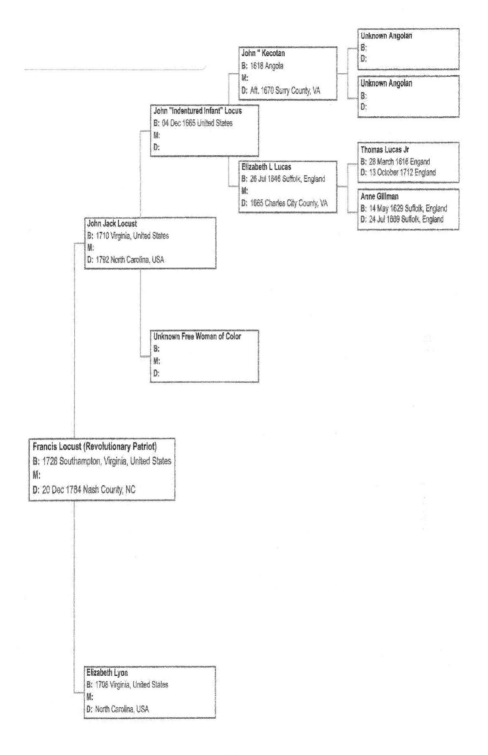

**John " Kecotan**
B: 1618 Angola
M:
D: Aft. 1670 Surry County, VA

**Unknown Angolan**
B:
D:

**Unknown Angolan**
B:
D:

**John "Indentured Infant" Locus**
B: 04 Dec 1665 United States
M:
D:

**Elizabeth L Lucas**
B: 26 Jul 1646 Suffolk, England
M:
D: 1665 Charles City County, VA

**Thomas Lucas Jr**
B: 28 March 1616 Engand
D: 13 October 1712 England

**Anne Gillman**
B: 14 May 1629 Suffolk, England
D: 24 Jul 1669 Suffolk, England

**John Jack Locust**
B: 1710 Virginia, United States
M:
D: 1792 North Carolina, USA

**Unknown Free Woman of Color**
B:
M:
D:

**Francis Locust (Revolutionary Patriot)**
B: 1728 Southampton, Virginia, United States
M:
D: 20 Dec 1784 Nash County, NC

**Elizabeth Lyon**
B: 1708 Virginia, United States
M:
D: North Carolina, USA

# Family Group Sheet for Caroline Carrie Locust

| Husband: | Peter Warters Fuller |
|---|---|
| Birth: | 1808 in Norfolk, Virginia |
| Marriage: | 25 Jan 1881 in Yazoo, MS |
| Death: | 09 Jun 1885 in Norfolk, VA; Died of old age |
| Burial: | Norfolk, Norfolk City, Virginia, USA |
| Father: | |
| Mother: | |

| Wife: | Caroline Carrie Locust |
|---|---|
| Birth: | 1806 in Robeson, Cumberland Co, NC |
| Death: | 26 Nov 1894 in Norfolk, VA; Living at 226 S. Halls St, Norfolk, VA |
| Burial: | Norfolk, Norfolk City, Virginia, USA |
| Father: | Isham Locus Lucas Sr. |
| Mother: | Margaret Maggie Roberts |
| Other Spouses: | James Medly (1835 in Wilson, North Carolina) |
| | Nn Jackson |

**Children:**

| 1 M | Name: | Richard Locust |
|---|---|---|
| | Birth: | 1833 in Kinston, Lenoir, North Carolina, USA |
| | Marriage: | 1869 in Nash, NC |
| | Spouse: | Esther Caraway |
| | Other Spouses: | Charlotte Hardy (19 Jan 1882 in Lenoir, North Carolina, USA) |

| 2 F | Name: | Jane Gatsey Locust |
|---|---|---|
| | Birth: | 1839 in Nash County, North Carolina; Listed as Mulatto on 1850 Kinston Census |
| | Marriage: | 1880 in Pitt, NC |
| | Spouse: | David Davis |
| | Other Spouses: | William Tayborn (21 Nov 1858 in Nash co., NC) |

| 3 F | Name: | Eunice Fuller Bradshaw |
|---|---|---|
| | Birth: | Feb 1844 in Grifton, Pitt, North Carolina, United States |
| | Death: | 1923 in Goldsboro, Wayne, North Carolina, United States |
| | Burial: | 1923 in Parkstown, Wayne, NC; Old Mill Cemetery |
| | Spouse: | Samuel Walter Jackson |
| | Other Spouses: | Nn Bradshaw |

| 4 M | Name: | Thomas Locust Fuller |
|---|---|---|
| | Birth: | 21 Apr 1847 in Grifton, Pitt, North Carolina |
| | Marriage: | May 1870 in Pitt, Lenoir, NC |
| | Death: | 03 Nov 1932 in Kinston, Lenoir Co, NC |
| | Spouse: | Manerva Nerva Dawson |
| | Other Spouses: | Beady Coward (15 Feb 1877 in Greene, North Carolina, USA) |

**Notes:**

Thomas Locust Fuller

# Contents

# Preface

Thomas Locust Fuller is my Melungeon great-great-grandfather. Thomas enlisted in the United States Colored Troops (USCT) on his 18th birthday. He struggled for years to obtain his military pension as his health deteriorated. Thomas' Melungeon ancestors were Catawba, Cherokee, and Lumbee Indians. His ancestors descended from Angolans in Jamestown and were "Free Born."

This historical and genealogical work chronicles Virginia and North Carolina Lucas, Locust, Kecotan, Lucie, and Roberts families. They trace their lineage to colonial ancestors who were Indigenous, African, and English. Though Melungeon roots are proven through DNA, their origins still foster heated discussions, disputes, and Portuguese ancestry.

These ancestors lived in Colonial times and fought in the American Revolution, the War of 1812, and the Civil War. Thomas's family defied many challenges. Being "Free" did not exempt them from indentureship in infancy, forced into military service, paying discriminatory taxes. They were also subjected to numerous lawsuits, burglary, and being physically attacked and beaten. At the same time, individuals kidnapped them and their children.

Thomas's Melungeon families originated in Angola and England. They "resided in Charles City County, Virginia. Elizabeth Lucie, a British servant maid, was presented by the churchwardens of Weynoke Parish for having an illegitimate child by an 'unknown' father." Her son, a "molotto boy the sonne of Elizabeth Lucie dec'd," was bound to Howell Pryse on 4 December 1665. His father was Jack (John1 Kecotan), "a negro servant to Mr. Rice Hoe," ordered freed from his service on 8 February 1665/6 by a note given him by his former master, Rice Hoe, Sr. [Orders 1655-65, 601, 617, 618, 632] after 29 years of indentureship".

"John1 Kecatan, born about 1618, (was in colonial America and indentured to Rice Hooe Sr. in 1635). The court ordered John set free in February 1665/6 [DWO 1655-65, 601, 604, 605, 617, 618]. He was probably the "Jack negro" taxable on two persons in Surry

County in 1670 [Magazine of Virginia Genealogy, vol.2, no.1, 23]. Many of John Kicotan's descendants served in every American war.

Their history and lineage began when the family first arrived from Angola in 1619 with their great-grandmother, Margaret Cornish. This journey highlights extensive genealogical research and constant motivation by a family surname mystery. It leads to searching for the identity of Thomas's wife, Manerva "Nerva" Dawson, whom many had forgotten.

The research consisted of travel to many libraries, State and National Archives, courthouses, vital records offices, cemeteries, etc. Information gleaned from combined historical data, oral and written family histories, wills, census, marriage, death, land, and court records. United States Army military pension records and affidavits documented Thomas, Isham, and Ishmael's patriotic services.

"Thomas the Melungeon" provides educational and genealogical information to young adults who might have been unaware of this period of American history. It examines the history of Free Persons of Color in the American Civil and Revolutionary Wars. This text provides hope to all of us who believe in justice and desire to embrace factual history. It helps us realize why we should be appreciative of our ancestors.

# ACKNOWLEDGEMENTS

I would like to thank the African American Civil War Memorial Museum staff in Washington, DC, for relating my great grandfather's and other Union Soldiers' stories and place their names on the Honor Wall. A special thank you to them for issuing beautiful Certificates in each soldiers' honor. I am also highly appreciative of my fellow sisters in the Daughters of Union Veterans of the Civil War for their support and encouragement.

Among a genealogist's greatest assets are the Libraries, Court Houses, Archives, and Vital Records Offices that house the valuable documents needed to verify one's ancestors' stories. These organizations make records readily available to researchers.

I am indebted to the following libraries: National Archives Washington, DC; Rockefeller Special Collections Library, City Library of Williamsburg, VA; Library of Virginia, Richmond; Newport News Virginia Special Collections Library; the Daughters of the American Revolution Library DC, North Carolina Archives Genealogy Library Raleigh, NC and the John G. Germany Genealogy Library in Tampa, FL (all of whom hold a copy of this book on their research shelves); the Wayne County Court and Deeds Records Offices Goldsboro, NC and Internet Archives Records which aided me in telling Thomas and his family's stories.

Many of Parkstown-Kinston, North Carolina cousins provided me with documents, pictures, and information about Thomas and Eunice Locust Fuller and their descendants. Many cousins engaged in extensive discussions making this book more than a vision but a reality.

I am incredibly grateful to my cousin, Marshall Jackson, who searched numerous North Carolina records and provided sources about our Fuller ancestors and my Best ancestors. Thanks to my Lucas/Locust Fuller cousins: Lula "Tootie-Pie" Best Atkins, Donnell Jackson Powell, Jean Cox Parks, John Wise, Carolyn Arthur, Stanley Davis, Doug Rowe, James Fuller, Robert Fuller, Charles Fuller, Lovely Fuller Dawson, Shakisha Mounsey, Ruth Dixon, Elaine Jackson, Louise C. Fuller, Malenis Holloway, Hobert D. Holloway, Louise

Fuller Holloway, Sykia Thompson, Keisha Barnes, and Teresa Frierson.

A special thank you to a diligent researcher and fellow genealogist, Tyrone Foye. Carol Curtiss and Cynthia Purdy patiently assisted me in the editing process. My sincere appreciation to my Lucas/Locust cousin, Floyd Jones, and his parents, who helped me verify my direct lineage to them through DNA.

I am also grateful to my Bunch-Locus cousins, Janice Locus Kent, Sam Joyner, Europe Ahmad Farmer, and Ninah Harris. They walked me through the complexities of the Gedmatch DNA Ancestry Project. I appreciate my cousins who shared their DNA with me, which helped me verify my Locust, Bunch, Grice, Best, Fuller, and Jackson ancestry.

**Antique Rocking Chair Made by**
**Thomas Locust Fuller**
**Courtesy of L. Fuller's Personal Collection**

## Bigmeat

Farewell, my beloved matriarch, going on to glory and
summoned forever from our midst.
Can we continue on our disquieted way without your
Grace and blessed angelic songs?

As you kneeled daily to pray with our names
Lifted in supplications, you offered us to the Lord.
You asked that He guide our way with His protective
Armor presented against vicious spear-like words,
That cut us from your loving care.

Inheriting gifts of wisdom to discern from our
Ethical or unjust deeds.
We spent pleasant summers there,
Learning strength and not to harbor fears
As God, be with us.

For you loved us so unselfishly.

Patient with our faults and growing pains,
You encouraged us to believe in a God who guides our path.
Now that you have gone, we fall to our knees and lament,
"God, who will pray for us now?"

Gigi Best

©11 Jan 1995

"Knowledge and DNA gleaned from factual history validates
our similarities and negates our differences."

Gigi Best

# CHAPTER 1

## Thomas and Bigmeat's Beginnings

Thomas Locust Fuller, a brave young man, enlisted in the Civil War on his eighteenth birthday. A descendant of many Free Men of Color Revolutionary War Patriots. As a "Free Man of Color," a farmer and a soldier, he raised his family as best he could in his era.

Thomas' lineage reaches back to Virginia with his 5th great-grandparents. One ancestor was Margaret Cornish, who originally arrived in the Colony in 1619 from Angola, Africa. She originally resided on the lower side of the James River at the Puritan Edward Bennett's plantation near the former Indian town Warraskoyack. Thomas's paternal great grandfather was an African man who lived in Colonial America as early as 1635. John "Jack" Kecotan and his family originated in Angola, Africa, in 1618. "Jack was held as an indentured servant of the Hooe family of Charles City County, Virginia, for twenty-nine years as of 14 October 1665." In 1653 he appealed to the Governor and Council of Virginia for his freedom.

Thomas' 5th great-grandmother, Elizabeth Lucie Lucas, was born in England in 1646. She indentured herself to the Hooe family as a servant maid. The child she had with Jack was indentured as an infant when she died in late 1665. Once this son, John, was free from his indenture, he had a daughter, born around 1696. She then had several children in Virginia, and Francis Locust, his 6th great grandfather, eventually moved to North Carolina.

This Free Woman of Color had a son named Francis Locust, born in Virginia in 1728. She lived there before relocating to Edgecombe County, North Carolina, between 1755 and 1759. Francis relocated to North Carolina because his neighbor continued to take him to court and force him to pay discriminatory taxes on the two Women of Color in his household.

"In June 1759, Francis was one of Edgecombe County's freeholders, North Carolina, ordered to work on Bryant's Creek's road to the Granville line. Francis received a grant for 525 acres on Turkey Creek in Nash County, North Carolina, on 9 October 1783. On 1 November 1784, Francis acquired another 150 acres on the south side of the creek.

Francis's daughter, Jane Locust, had three children who were indentured because they were born outside of wedlock. Those children were Isham, Burrell, and Martha Locust. One of Jane Locust's sons, Isham Locust (an War of 1812 Patriot), is Caroline Carrie Locust's father.

The Locust family were Melungeon with Catawba Cherokee origins, along with their African and European ancestry. Melungeons are said to be Tri-Ethnic people reported to be descendants of Native Americans, Turkish, Iberian, Portuguese, Africans, and Europeans. Thomas knew that he had multiple ethnicities, but he nor Isham could prove their Native American ancestry. Yet, family stories were present

as a spoken legacy. He could not remember most of the original Cherokee names or their language. He saw the physical proof in the high cheekbones, the thin lips, the prominent male nose, and the elongated head of the Catawba.

*Littlemeat and Bigmeat as Teens*
*Author's Collection.*

Free People of Color (Melungeons) did not intentionally want to bring attention to themselves when they lived in Virginia, so they left that State. They knew that the Anglo Virginians were now becoming more involved in slavery. These Virginians feared the Melungeons and thought that they might cause enslaved insurrections. A general concern was that they might spirit away the individuals held in bondage. The enslavers feared their enslaved would accompany the Free or Freed people as they left Virginia.

Thomas's family were those Free Persons of Color who left Virginia in the mid-1700s and relocated to North Carolina. His family was born into freedom during the enslavement of many people of African descent. He traces his Locust family lineage to his direct descendants, the Fuller family and Thomas' granddaughter, Rosetta Fuller.

Rosetta Fuller came into the world on September 12, 1905, bouncing and happy. This natural disposition carried her through life. She was a beautiful baby born with a reddish-brown tint to her skin, and her coal-black hair looked like someone had purposely styled it into a soft Mohawk. Her hair lay flat on the sides of her head and flipped up at the bottom, and her locks fell just past her ears into a soft flipped-up curl.

Thomas, like everyone who saw her, said she was remarkable. Like so many babies, Rosetta was not bald but had a full head of hair, and her head shaped slightly longer than most, but not enough to be unattractive. Thomas's daughter-in-law, Florence, knew her baby would be born with a head full of hair. Shee suffered severe heartburn while carrying her (reminiscent of an old wife's tale).

Though her name was Rosetta, Thomas nicknamed her "Bigmeat," which was ironic because she would grow to be barely over five feet tall. Her personality and demeanor made her "Big." Thomas gave her that name from the Cherokee Bigmeat family.

It was her nickname through life, and people who called her by it may not have known of its Cherokee origin. Everyone called her Bigmeat from the time she was a little girl, and when she was all grown up, she was called Aunt Bigmeat or Cousin Bigmeat, and her church members called her Mother Bigmeat or "Sis Bigmeat." Thomas's granddaughter was a happy child, and when she came into the world, the tiny house teemed with family.

Thomas's son, Daniel Fuller, and his wife, Florence Parks, were married on January 8, 1896, in Wayne County, NC. The 1900 census listed just five people in the home, Daniel, Florence, and their children, Lew, Luther, and Laura. Lew had married shortly before Bigmeat was born. Lula, nicknamed "Lew" by the family, recently married a young man named William "Bill" Britt. Bigmeat had seven sisters and brothers, and then two years later, she had a new baby sister, Lossie.

The 1910 U.S. Census listed eight people already living in the home: Thomas's son Daniel was 30 years old, his daughter-in-law, Florence was 28, his grandchildren were Luther 14, Laura 13, Herbert 6, Lossie 2, and Bigmeat was four years old.

Daniel and Florence then welcomed a cousin to live with them. Her name was Salista Body, and she was 15 years old at the time. Salista had lost her parents. In practice, usual for the time, the family stepped up and helped raise relatives and friends' children.

As soon as Lossie could walk, she and Rosetta were inseparable. Everyone called Rosetta "Bigmeat," and they called her little sister, Lossie, "Littlemeat." Lossie was the closest sibling to Rosetta. Now Bigmeat had someone she could love, like a little doll and protect.

In the 1920 U.S. Census, Bigmeat was a 14-year-old teenager and her sister Litttlemeat was 12 years old. Bigmeat's father, mother, brother Herbert, her sister Littlemeat, her brother Lamb, and her baby brother, Lapold, were at home. Also living with them were Thomas' great-grandchildren, Ella, Mildred, and Lizzie Fuller. They lived in a small crowded home filled with love.

Thomas's granddaughters, Bigmeat and Littlemeat, were not the only children in the family who had unusual nicknames. Thomas's grandson was named Luther, yet everyone called him "Rooster." Then Daniel named his son after his brother, Lemuel, whose nickname was Lamb, but when Daniel's son was born, they just named him Lamb.

One of Thomas' other grandsons' names meant Leopold since his parents did know how to spell Leopold; he was named Lapold. It was an unusual name, but there were many unique nicknames in the family.

Thomas' great-niece was fascinated with family and wrote a poem about family nicknames:

"There is one thing that has always fascinated me, and that is the nicknames in our family tree.

They are interesting, to say the least, cause they are royalty all the way to a beast.

There are some whose name has no meaning at all, and some whose nicknames are hard to recall.

Let me give you a sample of what I mean. We have not only a King but also a Queen.

There's a Coot and a Root, a Scob and a Rob, and the name Zephaniah who's called Uncle Bob.

There's Tet, Tee, and Tot, a female called Tom, Froggie, Captain, and Drew. There are Nate and Ced; can you believe Ava's dad is calling her Pooh?

There's a Nook and a Chib, Booby, and Gait. You think I am kidding? Why you just wait!

Cause there's Spoogie, Peter Rabbit, Scam, Lamb, and Mot. There's a Biggie and a Coonie. Why I kid you not!

We also have fowl. I'm informed that we do. There's a Rooster and a Chicken. Why it's just like a zoo!

Cause there's a Goat and a Pig, a Cat, and a Horse - A Possum, a Duck, and some insects, of course.

Like a Gnat, a Bug, and a wee little Tick - A Snook, and a Stank; you can take your pick.

Between Big Meat and Little Meat and just plain Meat - Little Baby and Honey who is ever so sweet.

There are Jack and Pudding, a Boo and a Skeeter - Stuckey, Nugget, and a guy called Deeder.

There's a Tweedy and Net and a Chicklet, too - Shell and Binkey, Tootie Pie and Fabu.

There are Peebaby and Peter, Sally and Doug - Dant and Pete and Chubby and Jug.

There's Big Bud and Little Bud, a Shug and a Jolly. That's not all; there's even more by golly.

Like a Lake and a Mu and the color Red; A Brother, a Sister – what more can be said?

Except for Little Gal and Big Gal, Bus Jess, and Si Rose - Who will come in the future? Only heaven knows.

If any name was overlooked, accept my apology; BUT tell me who can really recall all the nicknames in this family tree.

To say they're unique is an understatement and really putting it mild.

Cause the nicknames in this Jackson clan are most definitely w - i - l - d ......to say the least."

## FAMILY NICKNAMES

By
Gloria "Tom" Seenarine ©

Bigmeat and her sisters and brothers grew up on the small farm; they fed the chickens, fed their one cow, picked fruit and corn, tended the vegetable gardens, and went to school. When dismissed, the children ran around the farm barefoot and played games with their cousins. Then one by one, the children moved away.

Just as Littlemeat and Bigmeat began socializing, as they were going to the Fair, going to family picnics, and hanging out with friends and relatives outside of the home, something unexpected took place. Thomas's two granddaughters, Bigmeat and Littlemeat, were sixteen and fourteen years old, respectively, when he experienced the saddest moment of his and his granddaughter's young life.

Littlemeat was pregnant and unmarried. Her parents decided to help her through this trying time and aid her in raising her new baby. Bigmeat was excited about the impending birth of her new niece or nephew. She vowed to help her sister as best she could, along with her parents. The family's excitement about their new edition was short-lived because Littlemeat lost her baby and her own young life to childbirth.

Sadness engulfed Thomas's entire family. He had lost his granddaughter and expectant great-grandchild at the same time. Daniel and Florence had lost their daughter, and Bigmeat lost her baby sister and best friend. Littlemeat passed away because of Preeclampsia,

18

which was probably the same illness that took her grandmother, Minerva, Thomas's first wife, and Daniel's mother.

Littlemeat left the family and was gone much too early. Grief filled them, and Rosetta, her protector, was deeply saddened. She did not understand how her baby sister could leave her all alone. Bigmeat felt as if she lost a part of herself. Daniel and Florence experienced one of the worst events that could transpire with young parents, and that was having a child proceed them in death.

Later in 1923, Bigmeat and the family lived in Saulston Township, North Carolina, where she met an ambitious and incredibly handsome young man, Robie Best. He was from one of Goldsboro's most prestigious families. The Best's could trace their lineage back to 1569 in England. Robie asked Daniel for Rosetta's hand in marriage. Her father agreed and promptly applied for his daughter and future son-in-law's marriage license.

Robie was from a small family, unlike Bigmeat. He had two sisters, Minnie Best and Lola Best, who married two brothers. Minnie married Lee Bell, and Lola married his brother, Lawyer Bell. Robie's first cousin, Charity Best, the daughter of Aunt Polly, married another brother, Leslie Bell. An interesting fact was that all the Bell men's names began with an "L."

Chapin Best and Mary Jane Hamilton, Best of Goldsboro, NC, were Robie's parents. Robie's grandparents left his father, Chapin, and his mother, Mary Jane Hamilton Best, a land legacy. It would be appreciated for many generations and continues to exist. Chapin's father, Theophilus "Offie" Williams Best III, left him 40 acres of land and left his sister Polly an adjoining 40-acre plot. The land is described in Theophilus' last will, probated on April 18, 1903. These eighty acres of land became the family community of Best Grove, Goldsboro, North Carolina, that still exists.

Their father was the Anglo-American son of Theophilus Best II and Nancy Jane Daniel Best. Theophilus II's Probate records left Farabee "Fabbie" Best, an enslaved woman, to their father in 1857. As a Confederate soldier, Theophilus went to the Civil War. He was held captive by Union Troops as a prisoner at Hart's Island Prison in New York until the war ended. Four years after his return, he fathered Chapin (1869) and Polly (1870) with Fabbie Best, a freedwoman.

*Laura Fuller Wise*

*Lamb Fuller*

*Lula Fuller Britt*

*Rosetta "Bigmeat" Fuller*

*Lapold and "Edie" Davis Fuller*

*Luther "Rooster" Fuller*

*Thomas Locust Fuller's Grandchildren*

*All Photos: Author's Collection*

Mary Jane's father, Isaac Hamilton (a Free Man of Color), died intestate and left his wife, Phoebe Thompson Hamilton, to process his estate. Phoebe bequeathed Mary Jane and her ten sisters and brothers nine acres of land each. Minnie Hamilton Lewis, Nannie Hamilton Lewis, Patsy Hamilton Loftin, Penny Hamilton Croom, Tempy Hamilton Lewis, Lewis Hamilton, Eliza Hamilton, Roxy Hamilton, John R. Hamilton, Avey Best, and Zany Best Taylor. Mary Jane received a great deal of land. Her mother, Phoebe, settled Isaac's estate on November 11, 1904.

Phoebe often spoke of her deceased husband fondly and expressed that he was a wonderful man who included his two stepdaughters in his Will. Avey and Zany were daughters of her first husband, Harris Best, and received equal shares of Isaac's estate. One of their sons drove a taxicab, and her grandsons eventually owned their own taxicab company in Goldsboro. The Best, Fuller, and Hamilton families inherited an entrepreneurial spirit.

Reverend R. Becton married Rosetta Fuller and Robie Best on November 1, 1924, at the Fuller family home in Saulston Township, North Carolina. Their parents and family members attended their wedding. Ed Williams of Saulston Township, Elijah Baker of Saulston Township, and James Langston of LaGrange, North Carolina were witnesses to the marriage.

The newly married couple moved to Stoney Creek Township after their wedding. By 1930, they were living next door to Robie's father and mother. The couple soon had one daughter, Wilhelmina Best, born on March 31, 1925, a son Daniel "Dant" Best, born May 3, 1927; and Chester "Pete" Best, born September 9, 1928. Robie fathered another son from a previous relationship, R. B. Yelverton, who was born in 1924.

Robie and Rosetta decided to move to a new location where they could raise their children with more land than was available in the city of Goldsboro. Robie mostly wanted to move to an area where he would not be judged and subjected to the constant questioning and accusing glares of his family and neighbors. All who knew him thought of Robie as a stubborn man who was always stuck by his decisions, whether they were wrong or right.

He made a significant mistake that caused his father and mother grief and forced them to sell most of their land to keep him from being prosecuted. The crime he committed was putting his newborn infant daughter into a basket and leaving her on the doctor's doorstep. His decision affected the entire family and left his mother and father emotionally distressed. His mother, Mary Jane, was a sagacious woman who lived to be 100 years old. She tried to convince her son of his wrongdoing.

When Bigmeat's mother-in-law, Mary Jane, came into the bedroom, she did not see what she expected to see, her beautiful brown-eyed granddaughter. She saw where Bigmeat and the baby slept looked strangely barren as she watched the small bed. Mary Jane saw Bigmeat but did not see the new baby, Wilhelmina, or her son Robie.

Mary Jane asked Bigmeat, "Where is baby Wilhelmina and Robie?" Her daughter-in-law was crying uncontrollably and barely able to get out the words. She said, "Robie took the baby to Dr. William Bryant's house, and he does not intend to bring her back." Mary Jane could not believe what she was hearing. She knew her son was stubborn, but this act was more than stubborn-headedness.

Bigmeat worked for the doctor and his wife, and they were always kind to her and gave her items to bring home. Robie was jealous and thought the doctor was too kind to his wife. He began having suspicions that the baby was not his. His cousins and his family told him that Wilhelmina looked just like him and nothing like Dr. Bryant. Robie would have none of it, and he said he would not raise her in his home.

Thomas asked Bigmeat how she could tolerate her husband's behavior. Her response was: "I could insist that I keep my daughter and raise her alone, but where would we go?" Bigmeat loved her new husband profoundly. She felt as though she could not take care of her daughter alone. Most of all, she feared that her husband would mistreat or harm the baby if she kept her.

Dr. William Henry Bryant and his wife, Victoria Sadie Bunn Bryant, a nurse by profession, decided to adopt Wilhelmina. They were married a long time and did not have children of their own. They wanted to protect this beautiful little girl. Now fifteen years later, they took the opportunity to adopt Bigmeat's child since they were without an heir. Everyone knew that Wilhelmina did not look like the Bryant family. Her birth record reflected Robie Best as her father, and they changed her surname to Bryant due to the adoption.

When Thomas's granddaughter, Wilhelmina, came into the Bryant's home, they lived at 306 West Pine Street in Goldsboro. Dr. Bryant's office was on School Street, not too far from School Street School. Later Bigmeat's granddaughter and grandson attended this same school near their home before returning to Camden, New Jersey.

Not only did Dr. Bryant and Victoria give their adopted daughter a safe and loving home, but they also gave her everything she wanted. They spoiled her and gave her the best of educations. Wilhelmina wanted for nothing, had the best of everything, but still became impossible to control as she grew older.

Victoria Bryant, Wilhelmina's adoptive mother, died July 20, 1937, when Wilhelmina was twelve years old. It is hard to say where Dr, Bryant was when Victoria passed away because she died in a hospital in Raleigh, North Carolina, without his attendance. Her husband was not the informant on Victoria's death certificate. The completed section referencing her spouse noted that Dr. Bryant was her husband. Still, his first name was omitted, which was strangely odd.

Wilhelmina began acting out after Victoria died following a short illness. If her adoptive mother had been sick longer, maybe Wilhelmina would have had time to adjust to the situation. Nevertheless, there she was again, in a position without a mother.

A girl needs her mother, especially when she is approaching her teen years. Since her father did not know how to handle her, he did the best he could with her. When all else failed, he sent her away to boarding school. He chose the only alternative he had. Bigmeat felt it was too late to bring Wilhelmina into her and Robie's home. Their sons were eleven and nine years old at the time. They did not know about their sister, and there would have been too much to explain to them. It was a family secret everyone knew about but kept from the boys. How could the family now tell Dant and Pete at this late date that they had an older sister?

Wilhelmina attended college after she left boarding school. When she completed college, she returned to Goldsboro and immediately sought out her adoptive parents in Parkstown. Of course, she still desired to connect with her birth parents and her brothers. Understandably, Bigmeat and Robie wanted to help their daughter be closer to the family. So, they sent her to live in Camden, New Jersey, where other family members lived.

Thomas's grandson, Herbert, was asked to look out for his niece, Wilhelmina. He took care of the home Bigmeat rented for her and handled the maintenance. In Camden, Wilhelmina now had a family she could lean on, and she could spend time with her mother, Bigmeat when her mother came north.

Although Wilhelmina was secure in a lovely home with an uncle to look after her, she did not want to remain in Camden and returned to North Carolina. She had always felt a sense of loneliness and abandonment. She never understood why her parents treated her differently from her brothers. "Was it because she was a girl?"

Wilhelmina knew her mother favored boys. "Were boys of more value than girls?" She knew differently because she was intelligent and well-mannered and graduated from four years of college. Her brothers did not!

When she was twenty-seven years old, Wilhelmina fell in love with a handsome man from North Carolina, John Thomas Terry. They married on August 2, 1953, in Wayne County, North Carolina. He was very protective of her. They moved to New Jersey and lived comfortably. The couple never had children because Wilhelmina did not want to bring a child into a world where they could feel abandoned. Much of her future was pre-determined by Robie's stubborn act of giving her up for adoption at birth.

# CHAPTER 2

## The Parkstown Community

*Bigmeat by Peach Plum Tree at the Best Store in Parkstown, N.C.*
*Author's Collection*

In the early 1930s, Bigmeat and Robie moved to Parkstown, a small rural community in Lenoir County, right outside of Goldsboro, North Carolina. The homes in Parkstown had rural route address numbers and not street addresses, as they had in the city.

Thomas' great-grandchildren, who came from New Jersey every summer, discovered that all of the people in the small community of Parkstown were their relatives (except two families). It was quite some time before they knew about the small community's makeup. It was quite a different experience up North, though some of the family had moved there.

There was endless excitement ahead for Thomas's children and grandchildren because it was, after all, the '20s, when life was full of new adventures. The young people lived in Jersey and could travel easily on trains to New York City. The young Southern men and women joined dance contests at the Blue Note, where they wore numbers on their backs and selected the best dancers as their partners. The dance contests lasted for days. The participants wanted to earn extra money, sometimes dancing until their feet ached and had blisters.

These new city dwellers went to Harlem and enjoyed the dancing, art, literature, and lure of that time. The Harlem Renaissance was a time when people of African descent could express their creative selves. Southern men and women brought their talents, which they acquired in the South, up North. Freedom to express their creativity made for the appreciation of their abilities. When they were industrious, the women worked in sewing factories, and the men worked in restaurants and plants. They worked at Campbell Soup in Camden or on construction jobs in Camden County and Philly.

Bigmeat stayed in North Carolina, unlike both her sons, her daughter, two brothers, two sisters, uncles, aunts, and many cousins. She missed their strong family bond. Her mother, Florence, moved to Camden and her father tried to relocate, but he was a farmer. He could not tolerate the city's close confines. Thomas' son, Daniel, left his wife, Florence, in Camden, New Jersey, and returned to North Carolina. Daniel could not abide the city life and said, "He could never live so close to other people where he could spit out his window and hit his neighbor's house."

During these times, Bigmeat thought about Littlemeat always, and she missed her terribly. She never forgot her baby sister, and now she missed her whole family. She was so excited when her grandchildren arrived from Jersey for the summer. She wanted everyone to know about their visit. The best way she knew to show her pride and happiness was by placing an article about their stay in the *New Journal and Guide* social pages. Someone published the article about their visit on September 3, 1955.

Articles similar to these were part of the *Norfolk Journal and Guide*, published under the title "Goldsboro, NC," in the article written by Henry C. Mitchell. When Thomas's great-grandchildren finally arrived in Parkstown, they immediately noticed the differences between Jersey and Philly and their grandparents' community. It was the experience and excitement of extra space, security, and safety. The children could kick off their shoes and run barefoot, which was out of the question in Camden.

They could run an errand for their grandparents by just going a couple of houses down the road and picking up big tubs of freshly churned butter. They only walked a few steps to their grandparents' store, or they just crossed the street to play with their young cousins. All of the churches were within walking distance.

It was a uniquely different way of life for the children in Parkstown because they could walk around their grandparents' farm. There they saw cows and were able to get fresh milk and helped feed the chickens. When they were ready for a chicken dinner, Grandmom Bigmeat would select a plump chicken and chop its head off on a wooden tree stump. The city children would then run around screaming and hollering because they thought the chicken was chasing them.

Bigmeat would visit her grandchildren in Camden, New Jersey, traveling from North Carolina on the train. On one occasion, she brought a live chicken to Camden on the train with her. When she gave the chicken to the family, her daughter-in-law (having been a country girl herself) wrung its neck in the bathtub. That act shocked one of the grandchildren who said that he "wasn't going to eat **a dead chicken!**"

The experiences of farm life provided the Northern grandchildren the opportunity to watch their Grandmom Bigmeat use one of her many skills. It was making that strange-looking brown lye soap in a massive cast-iron vat. The giant vat was used to wash clothes with the assistance of a big stick. Bigmeat pushed the long pole up and down to agitate the clothes as the vat sat over a hot flame. She then placed the clothes into clean hot water to rinse them, wrung them, and then hung them on the clothesline to dry.

In the 1950s, there was no indoor bathroom, just an outhouse that the city children feared going to at night. They even feared using it in the daytime because they heard of snakes that would come up and bite them. Their mother told them stories of snakes that came into the yard and crawled down a baby's throat because they smelled the baby's milk. The children were also afraid of the tobacco worms and grasshoppers that seemed to be everywhere.

Various fruits were growing on the farm, which consistently enticed them to consume as many as possible. Those delicious deep purple Muscadine and light green Scuppernong grapes grew on giant vines in the back of the house. These most scrumptious grapes had a rigid exterior hull. When the children sucked the insides out, they could not believe the incredible taste. They had never tasted anything like them up North.

There were two types of melons growing on the farm: green and the other white, but they were both sweet. Many kinds of fruit trees grew there and were readily available for picking. There were the pecan trees, from which Bigmeat picked nuts and packed them into small boxes each November. She either mailed or delivered them personally to her grandchildren in New Jersey.

The most desirable fruit tree on the property was a Peach Plum tree that grew near the family's General Store. The peach plum had a unique flavor to it. It was as if peach and a plum kissed and combined each fruit's unique flavor because it was juicier than both. It was a succulent fruit, and if it hit the ground, it splattered its sweet purple juice everywhere.

When Bigmeat took her grandchildren to church, they found it challenging to keep their minds on the church service, as lively as it was. Returning home, they saw evidence on the driveway. They realized that their cousins had been shaking the tree to claim some of that beautiful fruit for themselves. Deep purple splotches covered the ground as if little fruit bombs had exploded everywhere.

While they were at church, the grandchildren barely could contain themselves because they feared that there would be no fruit left for them. In New Jersey, they attended Ferry Avenue Methodist Church, where the Pastor spoke in soft tones. The Melodic choir sang hymns that were slow and deliberate. However, in Grandmom Bigmeat's Church, there were exciting songs and holy dancing.

It was a vibrant and exciting church service, not quiet at all. The Pastor, Reverend Dunn, preached like an engine that started slow and increased in sound and magnitude. The children enjoyed his "call and response" style. He carried a handkerchief with him and continually wiped the sweat from his brow. As he preached, he inhaled in deep breaths after a string of words and subsequently wiped the sweat from his forehead in a patterned style.

Reverend Dunn did not stay in one place like the Methodist Minister, Reverend Bagley, did. He walked back and forth on the Dias and took deep audible breaths between his sermon's words. It seemed rehearsed when the choir would chime in. The "Amen Corner" would validate his preaching style by agreeing in unison with his terms.

As the crescendo rose higher and higher, the drummer would chime in with rhythmic beats, and the women would jump to their feet and begin "shouting." The service was so enthralling to the children that they forgot about the peach plums until they went home.

Parkstown was a community of very religious people, and many of Thomas' relatives had their churches there. Thomas's grandchildren and other relatives either attended Saint Delight Holiness or Mount Zion Seventh Day Adventist churches.

Bigmeat's granddaughter and her cousin Tootie-Pie Best used to argue whether God rested on Saturday or Sunday. Of course, it was just the friendly disagreements of small children. Their cousins, Marshall Jackson and Donnell Jackson lived close by and attended Mount Zion Church and Tootie-Pie.

Grandmom Bigmeat drove her grandchildren around in her significant, beautiful, long, black, shiny 1964 Buick Electra 225, which was known as a "Deuce and a Quarter." The children loved riding in that car because their family only owned a 1949 Black Chevy for a family of eight at home in Jersey. Bigmeat also let them ride in the back of their granddaddy's truck when they worked on the farms.

Bigmeat attended the Holiness church and took her grandchildren with her early on Sunday mornings as she did for their father and uncle when they were children. They arrived at church early to attend Sunday school. She taught the teenage class, and her grandchildren, though much younger, were also allowed in her class. After Sunday school, they stayed for the regular church service. Next, they drove to another church for an afternoon service. Those church visits made for a very long day.

The children enjoyed meeting other children their age at the churches they visited. The favorite portion of those long days was the food. The church member brought Carolina pulled pork, fried chicken, potato salad, fresh biscuits, homemade pineapple, and lemon pound cakes, sweet potato pies, banana pudding, and that wonderful coconut cake with coconut icing and many other delicacies, all "southern and delicious."

Family members built Saint Delight Church before Bigmeat was born. The original church had a wooden structure with a potbelly stove positioned in the middle of the room. When Bigmeat and the other women in the family church started doing that dance, they call "shouting" (their way of praising the Lord), the floorboards would vibrate and shake with joy. The choir would sing, and all the family in the little church would clap their hands and stomp their feet, and some would "get happy and cry tears of joy."

Bigmeat was a Field Missionary and traveled from County to County, spreading her love of "The Lord." She opened the doors of Saint Delight for Friday night prayer for many years. The first Friday after she passed away at 89 years old, the church missed her presence. Bigmeat held many leading roles in the church. She loved working with youth and was a leader in the Eastern District Y.P.H.A, the Eastern District Union, and the Old Mill Cemetery and Burial Club.

Bigmeat had a beautiful melodic voice and held senior Choir president's office for more than forty years. When she was in the choir, she would "shout" also. For small children, not used to seeing that type of praise, it terrified them. They wondered why their Grandmom Bigmeat was behaving in that manner. Tears came to the little ones' eyes, and they wept nonstop because, in New Jersey, they never saw such a thing.

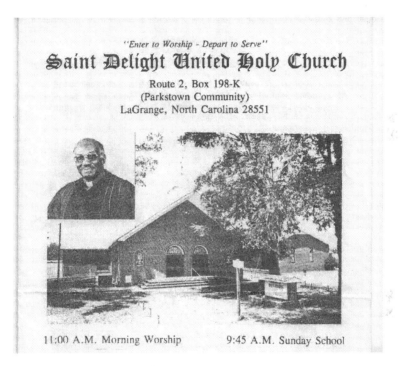

*Saint Delight United Holy Church*
*Author's Collection*

Thomas's great-grandchildren thought that their grandmother might have been sick. They did not know what was transpiring, but as they got older, they began to understand. They also remembered when Grandma Bigmeat visited them in Jersey; she danced, coming through the door and performing the same "Happy Dance" she did in the

31

church. Then they knew that she started shouting because she was so happy to see them, as she was pleased to praise "God."

By: Jean Cox Parks

"Saint Delight Holiness Church, established in 1900 with a small group of people. This group consisted of John and Liddie Parks, Ben Eddie and Tempie Lewis Hardy, Marie Worrell, and a few others who had taken a stand to go deeper in the Lord. In 1901, the church got its first pastor, Rev. David Atkinson, and under his leadership, the group built a small church, naming it Saints Delight Holy Church.

Under Rev. R.D. Brown's leadership, the congregation built a larger church next to the old one. In January of 1933, a tragic fire destroyed both churches. There was no amount of hardship that would stop this group of dedicated saints from worshiping their God. They took sheets and sacks and built a shelter in which to worship.

A third church was built a few months later, under the leadership of Rev. Adam Scott. In 1936, Rev. B.B. Dunn became our pastor and served faithfully for Saint Delight Holy Church. It continued to grow both spiritually and financially for 37 years. The church constructed the present sanctuary in 1964.

Under the leadership of Elder Leamon Dudley, our 12th pastor, a newly constructed addition occurred in 1974.

Our beloved pastor consecrated to Bishop on September 20, 1985. Bishop Dudley continues to be our Pastor today.

We thank him for 32 years of dedicated services rendered to the officers and members of Saint Delight Holy Church."

Many family members left Goldsboro and Parkstown and moved up North during the thirties to begin a new life away from the farms. They tended to gravitate towards each other. However, Robie and Bigmeat decided to put roots down where they were.

The rural area of Parkstown seemed like the right choice for them to set up residence. Robie's act of selfishness associated with his father's land inheritance determined their move from Goldsboro. Robie had squandered his legacy with his stubbornness. Consequently, he went to a family friend to borrow the money needed to purchase a land plot.

They purchased this land from Bigmeat's cousin, MaxiVara "Vera" Jackson Parks, Daniel's first cousin. Thomas's son, Daniel, was raised with her. Another cousin who helped them build their home was Robie's first cousin, Dock Best, a carpenter by profession. Several of Robie's cousins were also carpenters. Robie's Aunt Polly's children learned the construction trade from one another, and many descendants still practice it today.

Another statement taken from the Parkstown Herald about Bigmeat and Robie's home was this notation:

"At some point, there are 195 houses in Parkstown. Mr. & Mrs. Robie Best built the first house in the heart of Parkstown on Parkstown Road. Robie's cousin, Dock, built their home in 1934, and it still stands at 1253 Parkstown Road. Marshall Jackson, Rosetta's cousin, is now the proud owner of the property."

Shortly after Robie and Rosetta built their home, they made a small general store on their property next to the house. It was one of the favorite meeting places in the community. Robie strategically positioned a "gossip" bench on the right-hand side of the store entrance. Robie would entertain his wife's male cousins when he was not serving a customer. The men would tell stories about their jobs, relatives, people they worked for, or whom they worked in the fields and on the farms.

The men sat outside and participated in conversations and jokes for hours. They sat on the bench for a while, and then somebody would leisurely head back down the road to his home for dinner, and the group would break up until the next day. The store was open six days a week, and Robie was there every day except Sunday. He had to rest that day because Bigmeat would not allow him to open the store on "God's Day."

As a local merchant, Robie's store sold everything, from cookies "as big as your head" to those sugary sweet Nehi sodas and honey buns. He sold small brown paper bags of peach plums for a nickel-a-bag. He even sold tires, fan belts, car parts, and gas. Robie received a certificate from the Shell Oil Company for selling their gas for over 35 years.

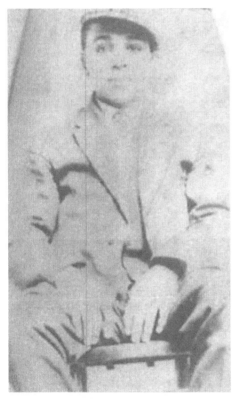

*Robie Best as a Young Man*
*Author's Collection*

Men would roll up to the store in their 1949 to 1956 cars and trucks and purchase gas. If they had a problem with their fan belt, they could purchase it from Robie also. Women often drove the big trucks as they took groups of family members and friends out to the farms to hand tobacco or pick cotton.

The women would work inside big tobacco barns where they "handed" tobacco. "Handing" was a process of taking a few leaves, placing them together, and tying twine around the stem at the top of the large green leaves. The rows of tobacco hung up to "cure" in the tobacco barn until they turned brown. The grandchildren could do light work in the barns or fields and earn extra money for their new fall school clothes during the summer.

Since most of the family members were farmers or farmhands, they would stop by Bigmeat and Robie's store and pick up the pre-packaged sandwiches wrapped in cellophane that they sold. They also purchased small blocks of dark yellow cheddar cheese or Nabs for their lunches while working on the tobacco farms or cotton fields.

Robie's uncles and cousins on his father's side had their businesses, and he wanted the same independence. He began his business by going door to door in his car to neighbors and relatives' homes. He sold candy, milk, and other products people wanted. He drove to Baltimore, Maryland, to get supplies to trade in his portable sundries business.

Eventually, Robie had enough money to begin stocking his little store with the tin roof. Some of Bigmeat's cousins did not like him because they believed that he should award relatives a discount or give children candy for free. He was steadfast in his refusals because he knew that the store was how he took care of his family.

Robie was a keen businessman and realized that most of his customers were his wife's family. He feared that he would go broke by giving away his profits. Though they were family, he could not give them his merchandise for free because he had to make money in this business for Rosetta, whom he fondly called "Zett." Robie built the place himself and was proud of his accomplishment as a General Merchant, and made a living from his store. It was a real feat for him because his father was a farmer.

Some family members said that Robie was "tight," When they said "tight," they meant they thought he was stingy. His wife's family claimed that he was so cheap that he took some money and buried it in the ground in a coffee can. When Robie returned to the location where he buried the money, it had deteriorated and was useless.

Nevertheless, the grandchildren loved their Grandfather because he was a quiet man and never disciplined them; only Grandmom Bigmeat did that. She occasionally made the children get a small switch from the tree if necessary to reprimand them. The discipline was only minor, just enough to get the children's attention; a lick from the tree on their palm was all.

One of Thomas's great-grandchildren took a cookie from the store when her grandparents were not looking. When her Uncle Pete told her grandmother of her indiscretion, she was humiliated. She had to get a switch, and her grandmother requested that she put out the hand with which she had taken the cookie. After a few stinging licks on her hand, the grandchild never took anything out of the store again.

Granddaddy Robie sat in a chair in front of the garage when he was not working in the store. When his health began to fail, his son insisted on closing the store, and Robie could only oblige, but he felt lost. The small store was his life, and when it closed, Robie still arose early in the morning, went out in front of the barn, and sat in his chair. He would then come inside to eat breakfast and go back to the same spot and to that same chair until dinner, and then he would go back in for supper.

After several months, he eventually died of, what some believe, was a broken heart. The doctors said it was a heart attack, but his grandchildren knew that he felt useless and had lost his reason for living.

Of course, Robie loved his "Zett," after all, they had been married over fifty years, but she was busy as a missionary and traveled a great deal and was gone all day Sunday.

The children also loved how their grandfather talked, like saying "Yesdiddy" for yesterday or pronouncing Friday differently than they did. He used the word "rack" for a hanger and "sack" for a grocery bag. He loved to eat chicken feet and fish heads. Their grandfather also dressed differently from the men up North. He wore bib overalls every day unless he went into town with their grandmother. Bigmeat, on the other hand, dressed more formally. She sewed her dresses and her church hats.

Their father's brother, Uncle Chester "Pete," Best had a wonderful disposition and joked with the children regularly. He told them that they would have to perform "second aid" on them when they fell and skinned their knees. Being inquisitive and knowing that they never heard of that remedy, they asked him, "What is second aid?" Uncle Pete told them that he would have to get a dirty rag, put more mud and oil on it, and wrap their leg in it to make it feel better. Of course, they eventually realized that he was just joking.

A small building on the property, situated in front of the barn, was where their uncle spent time working on things. This building is where he kept his phonograph records and collectibles. He was a Korean War Vet who had many stories to tell of his adventures. The children loved to explore this building and to take out the old phonograph and play records. Some of the song titles were amusing and kept them occupied for hours.

The grandchildren did not understand when they went to a department store with Grandmom Bigmeat. The woman behind the counter ignored them and would not wait on them. When they questioned their grandmother, she told them that People of Color had to wait in line until the clerk served all the other people in the store.

Though the children were young, this behavior did not sit well with them. This display of blatant partiality made them determined not to give anyone their money who did not show them the proper respect. They deliberately drank out of the "White" water fountain and not the "Colored" one because they knew that separating water fountains was not correct. They adopted their radicalism because they did not see those signs in New Jersey.

A story that their mother, Izzie Mae, told them always stuck with them. She shared a negative experience of visiting a restaurant in Elkton, Maryland. The staff objected to serving her until after all Anglo customers. Their mother chose to walk away. She lived in New Jersey and never was subjected to this abuse at a restaurant after leaving North Carolina. Like Grandmom Bigmeat, their mother always taught the children to walk with their heads up high, get a good education, and not let anyone down.

When the grandchildren were at the farm, some situations terrified them. As they played outside, they heard loud ear-splitting booms several times a day. When they asked their grandparents about these loud noises, they discovered that Wayne County was blowing up moonshine stills.

The children saw African American men with chains on their legs, all dressed alike, and came to get water from the family's external water pump. It saddened them to see these men in chains. The Anglo men held rifles in their arms to threaten the African American men from running away, and the children knew this behavior was not proper.

Their grandmother explained to them the system of prison peonage. She told them that immediately after slavery ended, the Sheriffs could accuse African American men of minor infractions and then arrest them. They were kept at the prisons to work on chain gangs to help alleviate taxes for Anglo Americans. The helpless prisoners were put into a symbolic slavery system again to the Counties. No one could help them obtain release. The prison system deemed the men as cheap labor, and many were abused and killed.

Another experience that the grandchildren shared in Parkstown was enduring the weekly requirement for them to drink half of a four-ounce bottle of castor oil. Once youngsters took their dose, they could go inside the family store and pick out any cookie or pastry they wanted. They were then allowed to choose their favorite bottle of Nehi soda to wash down the snacks.

Bigmeat understood her husband's role as the primary family breadwinner. Most women did not work outside of the home. The women helped on the farm, took in laundry or ironing, cooked mouth-watering food, and took care of their children and family chores. Bigmeat was a family Griot who shared genealogy with her grandchildren. She explained the relationships of the family who lived in the small Parkstown community. Bigmeat read the bible to her grandchildren and gave them continual religious instruction.

When they visited her, she told them that she asked their father to raise her grandson. Her son, separated from his wife, emphatically told her, "No!" He did not have the compassion for them that she did, and he should have had. Bigmeat told her grandchildren that she had asked for the boy because she favored boys, but she also loved the grandgirls.

Maybe Bigmeat wanted to raise her grandson because she had an empty nest and felt the need to nurture a child again. She never recovered from the loss of her sister Littlemeat and the guilt of not raising her daughter. Her sons were her life, even after they were grown. She raised her two sons and spoiled them so much that when their father, Robie, said they could not have something, she would sneak and give it to them anyway.

*Ruth, Les (small Child) and Jimmy Fuller and their grandfather,*
*Daniel Fuller, at Robie and Bigmeat Best's Family Store, Parkstown, NC*
*Author's Collection*

39

# Family Group Sheet for Thomas Locust Fuller

| Husband: | Thomas Locust Fuller | |
|---|---|---|
| Birth: | 21 Apr 1847 in Grifton, Pitt, North Carolina | |
| Death: | 03 Nov 1932 in Kinston, Lenoir Co, NC | |
| Marriage: | May 1870 in Pitt, Lenoir, NC | |
| Father: | Peter Warters Fuller | |
| Mother: | Caroline Carrie Locust | |
| Other Spouses: | Beady Coward (15 Feb 1877 in Greene, North Carolina, USA) | |

| Wife: | Manerva Nerva Dawson | |
|---|---|---|
| Birth: | 1857 in Pitt, Co. NC | |
| Death: | 22 Apr 1874 in Pitt Co., NC | |
| Father: | Benjamin Dawson | |
| Mother: | Rebecca Becky Dawson | |

## Children:

| 1 M | Name: | Rev. Lemuel Henry Lamb Fuller |
|---|---|---|
| | Birth: | 25 Dec 1870 in Kinston, North Carolina, United States |
| | Death: | 17 Apr 1928 in Wilmington, New Hanover, North Carolina; Age: 55y 3m 22d |
| | Marriage: | 1898 in Philadelphia, Philadelphia, Pennsylvania, United States |
| | Spouse: | Emma J Johnson |
| | Other Spouses: | Mary Anderson (01 Jun 1927 in Mecklenburg, North Carolina, USA) |

| 2 F | Name: | Fannie Fuller |
|---|---|---|
| | Birth: | 1872 in Grifton, Lenoir, North Carolina |
| | Death: | Bef. 1904 in Saulston Township, Wayne, North Carolina |
| | Marriage: | 28 Jun 1885 in Wayne, North Carolina |
| | Spouse: | Jesse H Seaberry |

| 3 M | Name: | Daniel Fuller |
|---|---|---|
| | Birth: | 21 Apr 1874 in Lenoir Co, NC |
| | Death: | 20 Oct 1956 in Wayne, NC; Buried in Old Mill Cemetery, Informant Rosetta Best (daughter) |
| | Marriage: | 08 Jan 1896 in Wayne Co, NC; Marriage to Florence Parks |
| | Spouse: | Florence Parks |

| 4 M | Name: | Guilford F. Fuller |
|---|---|---|
| | Birth: | 04 Jan 1878 in Lenoir County, North Carolina, USA |
| | Death: | Feb 1963 in Delaware, USA; Age at Death: 85 |
| | Spouse: | Mary Wife of Guilford Fuller |

| 5 M | Name: | Hardy Lincoln Fuller |
|---|---|---|
| | Birth: | 24 Nov 1879 in North Carolina |
| | Death: | 30 Nov 1933 in Kinston, Lenoir, North Carolina; Age: 54 |
| | Spouse: | Mary Magdaline Mamie Black |

| 6 M | Name: | Peter Garfield Fuller Sr. |
|---|---|---|
| | Birth: | 09 Oct 1881 in North Carolina |
| | Death: | 24 Dec 1973 in Kinston, Lenoir, North Carolina; Age: 92 |
| | Burial: | Kinston, Lenoir County, North Carolina, USA |
| | Marriage: | 1917 in Cheraw, SC |
| | Spouse: | Louise C. Talley |

40

| 7<br>F<br> | Name: | Rebecca Fuller |
|---|---|---|
| | Birth: | 09 Feb 1883 in Lenoir |
| | Death: | 13 Sep 1918 in Vance, Lenoir, North Carolina |

| 8<br>F<br> | Name: | Hattie Fuller |
|---|---|---|
| | Birth: | Mar 1885 in North Carolina |
| | Death: | 13 Jan 1933 in Grifton, Lenoir, North Carolina; Age: 47 |
| | Marriage: | 06 Jan 1907 in Lenoir, North Carolina, USA |
| | Spouse: | Oscar L Williams |

| 9<br>M<br> | Name: | Thomas Fuller Jr |
|---|---|---|
| | Birth: | 10 Apr 1889 in Lenoir, North Carolina |
| | Death: | May 1967 in Baltimore, Baltimore, Maryland, United States of America |
| | Marriage: | 06 Nov 1920 in Lenoir County, N/C |
| | Spouse: | Julia A Kelley |

**Notes:**

**Thomas Locust Fuller**

# CHAPTER 3

## Searching for the Fullers

It was April 21, 1874 - a gloomy spring day in Fountain Hill, Greene County, North Carolina. Members of the Fuller family had gathered in the home's front room, anxiously awaiting the birth of a new edition to the family. Thomas had returned from the war and married Minerva, a young neighbor girl. They were a happy young couple.

Their son Daniel came into the world under difficult circumstances. He had to fight his way through a complicated birth. He was living proof of stories that the elders spoke of where a baby can feel distressed in the womb. Daniel must have felt something wrong since he experienced the pain that his mother felt before his birth.

Daniel instinctively felt that it was hard on his mother, so hard that the midwife had to work feverously to bring him into the world. The midwife realized that this child could not be born quickly or safely because he was "Sunny Side Up." His head was facing up instead of down, maybe causing the baby's neck to break when entering the birth canal during childbirth. The midwife had to struggle to turn

*Daniel Fuller on His Farm*
*Author's Collection*

42

him around manually. When he came into the world crying, she did not have to spank his bottom to open his lungs.

Daniel was Thomas' and his wife, Minerva's third child. His sister and brother heard the new baby crying and listened to adults speaking in hushed tones in the room as family members paced back and forth and wrung their hands. Lemuel was only three years old, Fannie was just a month shy of two years old, and they were both so small that they were not sure what was happening with their mother. Their father understood their grief and attempted to console them.

Thomas could see that his son Daniel felt safe and warm lying on his mother's chest though he was just a few hours old. Minerva was distraught and in great pain, her swollen body with Preeclampsia. She felt the sadness in the room and knew the family was worried about her. There were cousins and grandparents present at the time. Later, when Thomas's children were old enough to understand, their father explained that their mother passed away the day after Daniel's birth.

Minerva passed away on April 22, 1874, and her husband, Thomas, was frantic. She was only 18 years old when she died, and Thomas was 26. Thomas had been willing to go to war but what he was facing took a different kind of courage.

When Thomas returned from his Civil War Army service, he decided to marry Minerva Dawson, a young girl he knew well. He married her in May of 1870. They immediately had three children, Lemuel "Lamb" Fuller, born December 25, 1870; Fannie Fuller was born May 9, 1872. On April 21, 1874, Daniel was born.

A complicated life existed for young Daniel because other women raised him in his family. It was incredibly tricky back in 1874 for his father, Thomas, since he did not know how he would feed his baby.

Every day that Thomas looked at Daniel, he could not help thinking about losing his beautiful young wife, who was no longer there. It was not as if he resented Daniel for surviving when his wife did not, but it was just impossible to clear his mind or his heart from the constant sorrow. The three children were difficult to care for because they were so young and needed a mother's care.

Immediately, a cousin, Julia Locust Outlaw, the daughter of his uncle, Richard Locust, born in 1822, stepped forward. She had a couple of children of her own by that time, so she nursed Daniel and kept him with her family. Julia also watched Lemuel and Fannie during the day while their father farmed. She nurtured Daniel along with her and her husband, Wright Outlaw's children.

Soon, Thomas could no longer stand the loneliness, so he wanted another life and decided to get another wife. On February 15, 1877, he married a woman named Beady Coward. When they began to build their home together, Thomas left his two youngest children with relatives. Since Lemuel, his oldest child, was seven years old at the time, he took him to live with him and his new family.

In 1880, Daniel was six years old, and Fannie was eight years old when they were living with a cousin, Rosetta Jackson Herring, and her family. In 1870, his cousin, Rosetta, was twelve years old, residing in his grandmother Caroline Locust's home with his Aunt Eunice and family. Thomas was not present in the house because he had left for military service and married in 1870.

*Florence Parks Fuller*
*Author's Collection*

Caroline Locust Fuller was Thomas's mother. Rosetta Herring's mother was Thomas's sister Cathy Jane Jackson, who was born in 1839. Jane was eleven years old when listed on the 1850 census with her mother, sister, and brother. Jane married David Davis in 1880 when she was 41 years old, and the 1900 census reflected that Jane had no additional children. Jane left Rosetta for her mother to raise while she went to find work.

Rosetta "Rose" Jackson married a man who was a minister, William Herring. It was in their home, Thomas's two children, Fannie and Daniel, lived in 1880. Rosetta and William had a son named James Robert Herring, who later became a minister in Chicago, Illinois. James Herring followed his father's example and continued the family legacy of a long line of ministers and missionaries. The Herrings also had a daughter in the home named Ely Ann. Again, Thomas's children had cousins their age to play with and close companions to share their thoughts and feelings.

Thomas's daughter, Fannie, married Jesse Seaberry on June 8, 1885. Though their marriage license said that Jesse was twenty-five and Fannie was eighteen, it was incorrect. Fannie was just thirteen years of age, having been born in 1872. Jesse Seaberry was Nicy Seaberry's son, a free woman of color, when listed on the 1840 and 1850 U.S. Census as a head of household in Wayne County, North Carolina. Fannie and Jesse's wedding took place in the Herring home, and William Herring officiated their ceremony. When Fannie died, her husband, Jesse, remarried.

Wayne County, North Carolina, 1880 census reflected Daniel and Fannie's grandparents, Peter Fuller and Caroline Locust Fuller. They were approximately seventy-two years of age and lived next door to their grandchildren. Since these grandparents were of advanced age, they really could not raise Daniel, who was, by that time, a very rambunctious young man.

When Daniel grew to adulthood, he married a beautiful young woman named Florence Parks on January 8, 1896; she was just sixteen years old at the time. Florence came from a small family, her father was Coleman Parks, and her mother was Susan Hinson Parks. The Parks family had been in Lenoir and Greene Counties for a long time. Since the Anglo-American Parks family owned a significant amount of property, farmers landowners, and were slaveholders in the area named for them; thereby, it became Parkstown.

Caroline and Peter Fuller were not able to care for their young grandchildren Daniel and Fannie. Their older grandchild, Rosetta, and her husband, William, chipped in to help. The advantage of living next door to their three grandchildren changed quickly due to life's circumstances. First, Fannie was married in 1885 and left home to begin her life with her new husband. Then Rosetta Herring and William moved to Chicago, Illinois, to try their fate.

The family moved to Norfolk, Virginia, where they had other family members. There were several descendants of the Locust and Fuller Free People of Color family living there. They also had Lucas family members who lived in Norfolk.

When the Herring cousins and the Fuller grandparents left Wayne County, North Carolina, other relatives took Daniel into their homes. It is unclear whether Daniel wanted to live with his father's new family or find it challenging to blend with them. Daniel's grandfather, Peter, died in 1885, and his grandmother, Caroline, died in 1894 in Norfolk, Virginia.

Rosetta Jackson Herring, her husband, William, and their children moved to Indiana. Thomas took Daniel to his sister, Eunice, who began raising him with her children. Eunice Fuller previously married a man named Bradshaw. In Wayne County, North Carolina, marriage license shows Eunice Fuller Bradshaw's marriage to Walter Jackson on October 20, 1873, Wayne County. Eunice's new husband, Walter, was a minister and a very handsome man. They agreed to take Daniel into their home and raise him along with their children.

Thomas' mother, Caroline Locust Fuller, was on the 1870 Census living with her husband, Peter, and the whole family listed by the surname Warters, including her granddaughter Rosetta. Recent DNA results show that Peter had been enslaved by his father, Thomas Warter's family. The 1880 census recorded the family by the Fuller surname when Daniel and Fannie lived next door to their grandparents in their cousin Rosetta Herring's home.

Caroline lived next door to Charles Fuller. That proximity appears to be why Peter chose the Fuller surname after emancipation. There

*Daniel Fuller, Ruth, Mildred, Esther and Gladys at Shell Gas Sign Robie's Store*
*Author's Collection*

is a myth that all enslaved people took the name of their enslavers, but records show a contradiction to this theory. Many enslaved people were upset with their enslavers. Some chose surnames that extricated them from their enslavers. Previously enslaved men made these decisions, either because of severe mistreatment or the denial of their biological connection by the parent or family.

Thomas was the father of nine children. Three children with his first wife, Minerva Dawson Fuller. He eventually had an additional six children with his second wife, Beady Coward.

Thomas' second son, Daniel, lived in the home with his cousin, Rosetta, when he was a small boy. Thomas chose his granddaughter Bigmeat's name to honor his cousin, Rosetta. Daniel and his sister, Fannie, loved Cousin Rosetta dearly because she took them into her home and nurtured them.

Hardy Lincoln Fuller, Thomas's third son, was born November 24, 1879. He was a farmer like his father, Thomas, and three of his brothers: Thomas Jr., Peter, and Daniel. Hardy married a woman that was from Lenoir County, Mary "Mamie" Magdalene Black. Hardy was the executor of his father, Thomas' estate, and aided Thomas in pursuing his military pension. Hardy died on November 30, 1933, in Kinston, Lenoir, North Carolina, at fifty-four from a tractor accident.

Rebecca Fuller, Thomas's second daughter, was born on February 9, 1883. She married Charlie Wooten, and then they divorced. She died on September 13, 1918, in Kinston, NC.

Hattie Fuller, Thomas's third daughter, was born in Kinston, North Carolina, on March 10, 1885. She married Oscar Williams, and they had 15 children. She died on January 13, 1933, in Kinston, NC.

In Kinston, North Carolina, Peter Garfield Fuller, Thomas's fourth son, was born on October 9, 1881. He attended Phillips, Gilbert, and then Savannah, Georgia schools, where he left after the sixth grade and then enrolled in Albion Academy. Peter completed four years of college at Hampton, University in Virginia. Studied Agriculture (majoring in Agronomy and Animal Husbandry), teacher training, and academics.

"After graduating from Hampton in 1913, he took charge of the agricultural program at a Negro orphanage in Riverdale, New York. Peter met his future wife, Louise C. Talley, there. She was also a teacher. They married in her hometown of Cheraw, South Carolina, in 1917 and had as least eight children. Peter and his family then moved to Bordentown, New Jersey. He began working at Ironside Industrial School. Peter was a farmer in Jersey City, New Jersey, in 1900. In 1920, he was a Church Sexton. In 1930, he was again a farmer in Princess Anne, Maryland, then moved to the Eastern Shore of Maryland and managed a large dairy farm.

Peter returned to Lenoir County before 1940, where he was a farmer and then later became the second African American County Agricultural Agent. He served as County Agent for twelve years, teaching resistant farmers new techniques to improve their crops. He organized many 4H Clubs and finally won over the local farmers with his expertise. Peter died on December 24, 1973, at the age of 92, in Kinston, Lenoir, North Carolina

Guilford F. Fuller, Thomas's fifth son, was born on January 4, 1878. He graduated from Albion Academy in Fountain Hill, North Carolina, in 1902. Previously named Albion Normal School, it was a

*Lemuel and Guilford Fuller's College Graduation from Albion.*
*Albion Academy 1901 Student Catalogue.*

teacher's college. He married a lady named Mary. On the 1920 census, Guilford was a cook at the Horn and Hardart at 1508 Market Street in Philadelphia. He was working for John Houston in Delaware and died there in February 1963.

Thomas Fuller Jr. was the sixth and youngest son of Thomas Fuller Sr. and Beady Coward. On April 10, 1889, he was born and married his wife, Julia Kelly, on November 6, 1915, when he was twenty-six, and she was sixteen years old. Their marriage license says that she was twenty because North Carolina required individuals to marry eighteen years of age.

Thomas Junior lost his wife when she was very young. Julia Kelly Fuller passed away at the age of 27. Much like Thomas Locust Senior, his son found himself without a wife to care for his small children. His four sons and one daughter lived with his older brother Hardy L. Fuller as shown on the 1930 Census. Thomas Jr. resided in Baltimore, Maryland, where he worked for a construction company and died there in May in 1967.

Thomas Locust Fuller Sr. ensured that his sons would be successful by insisting that they obtain good educations. At least three of his six sons received college degrees. Lemuel, Guilford, and Peter Garfield Fuller all attended Albion Academy. They were intelligent and mannerly men who were the sons of a Union Civil War Soldier. Being the son of a hero made them very proud. The school made them feel welcome    and    comfortable    in    their    new    environment.

Albion Academy, a Normal and Industrial School, was located in Franklinton, Franklin County, North Carolina. The school was on a property, "which commanded a picturesque view of the country for miles." About 150 yards from the Seaboard Airline Railroad's mainline, it was about a quarter of a mile from the railroad station. The Academy explained its school as follows: "This system is one of the finest in America. Its location is free from malarial and pulmonary diseases."

Admission requirements for candidates were stringent. Lemuel and Guilford could receive an excellent moral character certificate if they came from another institution. The sons were also provided a certification of honor, attesting that they received proper dismissal from their last institution.

All of his sons were required to attend daily prayers and needed to participate in religious services on "the Lord's Day." They adhered to "such exercises of instruction and recitations as were assigned the students regularly." After his sons advanced within their assigned courses of study, they returned promptly to the Academy at the next session's opening.

Albion told Thomas about their beginnings and about the many obstacles they had to overcome. They said that prayer, energy, and its founders' persistence gradually grew the school.

The State of North Carolina believed in having intelligent, warm-hearted citizens and their right to suffrage intelligently for their country's good. They thought the elevation of the race and the glory of God was essential to the Academy."

North Carolina established six Normal Schools, and they located one at Franklinton in connection with the Albion Academy. "The aim of the school and all its departments was to be thorough and practical to prepare competent consecrated workers who will meet the immediate needs of the people." North Carolin established the Normal Schools to prepare young men for higher colleges such as Lincoln, Biddle, and Howard Universities or any other of their choice.

Thomas brought his two sons to Albion Academy because "of its foundation on Christian education. It was also convenient for study, and it welcomed residents who complied with the conditions of admission."

Albion Academy's bill was only fifty dollars for students' courses once they completed their first-year study. Every student has to pay their bills if they were able. If Thomas's sons wanted their clothes washed, it cost either $.50 or $.75 per month, and their books cost about five dollars for the semester. Thomas's sons' expenses were various after the first session, and then the tuition was free.

Lemuel and Guilford paid for the wood they needed for their fireplace, it cost $.50, and board and washing were $16.60. The tuition was free for the second session, but the wood was $.75, and boarding and washing expenses were $27.15.

Albion was like most of the first schools created for African American children after the Civil War. The schools, sponsored by churches, were religiously based. Albion was not separate and was dependent on funds from benefactors. They aimed to prepare young men and women to be teachers in schools intended to instruct people of color in the Southern States. Organized by the late Rev. Moses A. Hopkins and Henry C Mayberry, its first principals respected by friends, North and South."

Albion Normal School had a dormitory, and Lemuel and Guilford's father incurred personal expenses for their board. Like all students, they were required to bring a lamp with them to school and supply it with oil. Thomas ensured that they bought the necessary towels, sheets, and pillowcases when they came for the semester. The medical expenses were the responsibility of the parents. If Thomas's sons became sick, he would incur a doctor's bill and medicine costs.

Albion's staff also stated, "They had many benevolent friends who were cooperating with the trustees and faculty in providing aid. Only for those worthy students who devote their time to study, and who would use their education for the good of others."

The Fuller family adhered to the Academy's suggestion proposed to all applicants. They applied for admission to the president, Rev. John A. Savage, DD. The faculty advised the students to use either the President or the faculty secretary, Ms. James W. Wilson.

The Fullers felt that it was more critical for them to apply straight to the President of Albion because they believed that they stood out in the community as an upstanding and honorable family. In their application, the school states the progress they had made in a previous study and their ability to meet education and boarding expenses.

Albion told Thomas, "Board furnished to the students in the Academy Boarding Hall on the school grounds was five dollars per month in advance." The school considered that "the board was good for the price" and that "no student needs to expect ten dollars board for five dollars." They also requested that parents and guardians note that the faculty refused to become responsible for students who boarded off the school grounds. Thomas and Beady decided that their sons would board on campus.

Industrial and Normal Schools were an essential asset to the African American Community during the Reconstruction period. They provided preparatory and primary courses. This allowed them to make a comfortable living for themselves once they graduated. The initial term enabled Lemuel to continue further progressive education as he advanced.

The Primary and Preparatory Departments also consisted of large group classes. The courses required at the introductory level were Bible Arithmetic, Mental Arithmetic, Written Geography, Grammar, Reading and Elocution, Spelling, Physiology, History of North Carolina, History of the United States, Penmanship, Music, and Industrial lessons.

*Picture of Best Grove Missionary Baptist Church and School Built in 1895.*
*Photographed by S.R. at the Best Grove Community Church, Goldsboro,*

The senior class members took a test to complete course studies at the close of the senior year. Lemuel completed the Normal Course and received a diploma. Guilford Fuller was in the fourth year of study and graduated in 1902.

Lemuel attended Albion Normal School in Franklinton, North Carolina, and graduated in 1896 at 26 years old. Albion was a preparatory school for African American students. Lemuel must have waited to enroll in college because he was there part of the same time his younger brother, Guilford, attended.

After graduating from Albion Academy, Lemuel transferred from Shaw University and enrolled in *Built* Lincoln University in Chester County, Pennsylvania. He was a freshman in 1896 and received his Bachelor's degree in 1899 at the age of 29 years old. Lemuel continued in his studies and acquired the equivalent of a Master's Degree in Divinity in its English Seminary Department. Lemuel graduated with an advanced Theological Degree in 1901 at the age of 31 years old.

Lincoln University began on April 29, 1854. Lincoln educated young men of African descent worldwide and did not admit women until 1952. The Theological Seminary's graduating class of May 1901

*Lemuel Fuller and his Graduating Class of 1901, Lincoln University, Chester, P.A. With 10 Fellow Seminary Students. Lincoln University Student Catalog 1902*

lists the graduates separately from the other students. The University was Christian-based, and all students were committed to adhering to those tenets.

"There is an assured prospect of students of an accession larger than usual to the classes of 1901 to 1902. The graduating class of the new 20$^{th}$-century year was constituted as follows for the full course." There were eight students in the Theology Full Course Curriculum graduating in 1901. One student was from Jamaica, two were from Pennsylvania, two were from Georgia, and three were from Virginia.

Lemuel always wanted to be an English teacher, so he concentrated on that curriculum while in Seminary. Lemuel was an English major and in that course. There were only three graduates for that year who majored in English. One student was Abraham A. Collins from California; another was Simeon Quann from Pennsylvania; and lastly, Lemuel H. Fuller from North Carolina.

In 1918 Lincoln University's Special Collections Catalogue had Lemuel H. Fuller's biography included. He was born in 1870 in LaGrange, North Carolina, the son of Thomas Fuller, a farmer, born "1850" in Kinston, North Carolina, and Minerva Dawson "1856" in LaGrange, North Carolina.

Lemuel attended Albion from 1894 to 1896, and then he spent one year at Shaw University. After he graduated from Lincoln University, he became Principal of Gould Academy in Chadbourn, NC. Lemuel was a pastor at three Presbyterian churches of the Cape Fear Presbytery. He was a Pastor at both Cape Fear Presbyterian Church and St. Matthews Presbyterian Church.

Another one of Thomas's sons, Peter Garfield Fuller, also attended Albion Academy before attending Hampton University. In 1898, while attending Lincoln University, Lemuel Fuller met and married Emma J. Johnson. She lived in Philadelphia, and they were married there before their move to North Carolina. After their graduation, they became teachers at Gould Academy, the only African American school in Chadbourn, North Carolina. Eventually, Lemuel became the Principal. Before 1920, the Board of Christian Education of the Presbyterian Church U.S.A. operated Gould Academy. It was organized into a school shortly after 1886.

Lemuel worked very hard, both teaching and preaching. The Fifty-third Annual Report for the Mission of Freedmen of the Presbyterian Church lists Rev. L. H. Fuller, Mrs. L. H. Fuller, and Miss Annie Hawkins as teachers of 220 students at Gould Academy in 1918. Lemuel learned a lot about running a school from the example he witnessed while attending Albion Normal School.

### Fuller Memorial Presbyterian Church Chadbourn, North Carolina

Cape Fear Presbyterian Church was founded in 1881 by Dr. Henry Clay Mabry and was later renamed Fuller Memorial Presbyterian as a tribute to the late Reverend Lemuel H. Fuller.

*Fuller Memorial Presbyterian Church, Chadbourn, N.C.*
*Cape Fear Presbytery USA Anniversary Catalog*

Thomas was incredibly proud of his son because Lemuel was very active in the Presbyterian Church and provided education to African American Students. Cape Fear Presbyterian was founded in 1881, later renamed Fuller Memorial Presbyterian. The church and school were a tribute to African Americans in Chadbourn, North Carolina. Fuller Presbyterian is no longer an active church. At least two previous female parishioners are still living. One woman is eighty-five years old, and another is nine-six years old, and both continue to live in Chadbourn.

Gould Academy is no longer a functioning school and existed until 1932. Many of its graduates attended Biddle, Lincoln, and Shaw Universities. Fuller Presbyterian Church was named for Thomas' son, the late Rev. Lemuel H. Fuller. Pastor Fuller held several prestigious positions in the Presbyterian Ministries. One of the jobs he had was Moderator at St. Matthews Presbyterian Church in 1920 in Dudley, North Carolina. He was relieved from that position when Reverend W. H. Best took over leadership.

Cape Fear Presbytery was the umbrella of churches under which Lemuel ministered. Cape Fear Presbytery began "its humble beginnings" at the Galilee Methodist Episcopal Church, Laurinburg, North Carolina, May 3, 1886, at 7:30 PM. A commission of the Atlantic synagogue comprised of several ministers met and organized the Cape Fear Presbytery.

The Presbytery was bounded on the North by Virginia, on the East by the Atlantic Ocean, on the South by South Carolina, and on the West by the North Carolina Counties of Durham, Person, Chatham, Moore, and Richmond. D. J. Sanders, elected its first moderator. The system comprised of 16 small churches with included: Bethany, Calvary, Chestnut Street, Davie Street, Ebenezer, First Fuller Memorial, Garnett Chapel, Haymount, Panthersford, St. Matthews, St. Paul, Second, Shiloh, Timberland, and Wilson Chapel.

Lemuel worked conscientiously and provided education to youth who needed new skills. He knew that these student's parents were forbidden to read and write while enslaved. He also realized that these unfair educational restrictions plunged a whole segment of society into forced illiteracy. The African American Community Church was the first organization to educate its youth.

The churches did the best to educate African American youth. However, they did not have the advanced texts and supplies needed for proper instruction. Subsequently, their descendants did not receive an equal education. They would not gain acceptance to integrated schools for another sixty-eight years.

The original church named for Reverend Lemuel Fuller burned on March 19, 1975. With all church records destroyed, the church purchased a new building later that year. The church was initially owned by Chadbourn Presbyterian and then by the Catholic Church. Chadbourn Presbyterian eventually honored Lemuel by giving the church the name Fuller Presbyterian Church.

Lemuel Fuller remarried after his first wife, Emma, passed away. He then married his second wife, Mary Anderson, on June 1, 1927, in Mecklenburg, North Carolina. Mary was a teacher, as was his first wife. Her first husband was also a minister, William Muldrow of Charlotte, North Carolina, who also passed away. Lemuel passed away one year after his marriage to Mary on April 17, 1928.

# Family Group Sheet for Eunice Fuller

| Husband: | | Samuel Walter Jackson |
|---|---|---|
| | Birth: | Mar 1847 in Fairfield Co. S.C. |
| | Death: | 07 Dec 1928 in Fork Twp, Wayne, North Carolina |
| | Marriage: | 1873 |
| | Father: | |
| | Mother: | |

| Wife: | | Eunice Fuller |
|---|---|---|
| | Birth: | Feb 1844 in Grifton, Pitt, North Carolina, United States |
| | Death: | 1923 in Goldsboro, Wayne, North Carolina, United States |
| | Burial: | 1923 in Parkstown, Wayne, NC; Old Mill Cemetery |
| | Father: | Peter Warters Fuller |
| | Mother: | Caroline Carrie Locust |
| | Other Spouses: | Nn Bradshaw |

## Children:

| 1 M | Name: | Willie Will Bradshaw Jackson |
|---|---|---|
| | Birth: | 1863 in North Carolina |
| | Marriage: | 1920 in Union, North Carolina |
| | Spouse: | Daisy Betty Parker |
| | Other Spouses: | Bulah Bradshaw (1893) |

| 2 M | Name: | Jesse Bradshaw |
|---|---|---|
| | Birth: | 1869 in Lenoir County, North Carolina, USA |
| | Death: | Arkansas, USA |
| | Spouse: | Ms. Bratcher |

| 3 F | Name: | Eunice Jackson |
|---|---|---|
| | Birth: | Feb 1872 in Lenoir County, North Carolina, USA |
| | Death: | Saulston Township, Wayne, North Carolina |

| 4 F | Name: | Ida Jackson |
|---|---|---|
| | Birth: | 22 Apr 1872 in North Carolina, USA |
| | Death: | 13 Jun 1960 in Goldsboro, Wayne, North Carolina, United States; Age: 88 |
| | Spouse: | James Milford Parks Sr. |

| 5 F | Name: | Maxivara (Vera) Jackson |
|---|---|---|
| | Birth: | 1874 in Lenoir, North Carolina, United States |
| | Death: | 04 Jul 1939 in Saulston, Wayne, North Carolina, United States |
| | Burial: | Jul 1939 in Goldsboro, Wayne, North Carolina; Old Mill Cemetery |
| | Marriage: | 25 Dec 1915 in Wayne, North Carolina, USA |
| | Spouse: | John Parks |

| 6 F | Name: | Mary Susan Jackson |
|---|---|---|
| | Birth: | Abt. 1878 in North Carolina |

| 7 M | Name: | Luby Albritton Jackson |
|---|---|---|
| | Birth: | 14 Feb 1887 in Saulston, Wayne, North Carolina, United States |
| | Death: | 07 Jan 1958 in Saulston, Wayne, North Carolina, United States |
| | Marriage: | 15 Jan 1908 in Goldsboro, Wayne, North Carolina |
| | Spouse: | Victoria Lewis |

# CHAPTER 4

## Locust-Fuller-Jackson Family

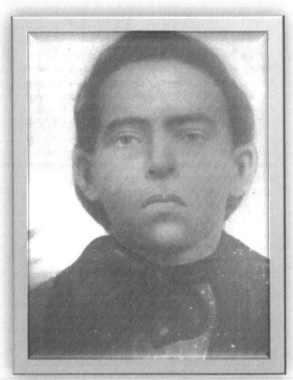

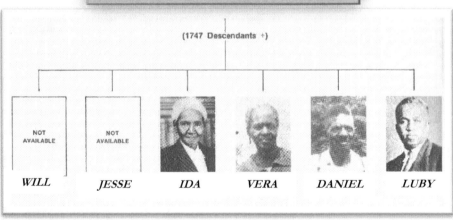

*Eunice Fuller Jackson and her Children.*
*Family Reunion Committee Booklet 1975*

Thomas's family occasionally spoke of their Native American heritage. They concealed the subject for generations. They just spoke of it in whispers, as if they thought that someone could hear them behind their closed doors.

Uneasiness still resided with them as they remembered the stories they heard from their ancestors. Thomas's ancestors feared being forced off their lands and carried away on that long, arduous journey known as "The Trail of Tears." The memory Thomas had with him was one of his ancestors walking long miles from North Carolina to Oklahoma and dying of exhaustion and starvation on the journey. His Cherokee ancestors' only alternative was hiding out in the woods, swamps, and mountains for fear of capture.

Thomas' family also knew from his grandfather, Isham, of the Catawba practice of "head flattening." This ritual consisted of a board being tied to the back of a child's head to reduce the elongated skull and make it uniform. He never observed this practice with his children or other family members. It was one of the ancient traditions and no longer practiced in his family.

When Daniel lost his mother to childbirth, he eventually entered his Aunt Eunice's home. He was later raised by her from six years old with her children, Will, Jesse, Ida, Vera, and Luby. In essence, he became another Jackson child and was excited about living with his cousins. Daniel had so much fun with them since they were near his age and were like brothers and sisters. He had plenty of love for his aunt Eunice and called her "Mu," as his cousins did. She was more than an aunt; she was his surrogate mother and loved him as if he were her own.

Daniel quickly became part of his Aunt Eunice's family since he often did not see his father. Daniel's father lived in Kinston, and Daniel lived in a different part of Lenoir County, dotted with rural farms. Thomas did not see his son much because he spent long days working on his farm, raising his crops.

Daniel's cousin Luby married Victoria Lewis on January 15, 1908, Isaac Lewis Sr. and Catherine Coley's daughter. Thomas knew his

*Luby Albritton Jackson with wife, Victoria Lewis Jackson*
*and Daughter Author's Collection*

ancestry and his nephew, Luby. Luby was a distinguished and dapper man. As a farmer, Luby was also familiar with his Native American and African American ancestors' ways. He knew things that others did not, and many family members trusted him to help them with difficult situations.

Luby Jackson and his family's picture shows his daughter wearing a jacket passed down through the family from his mother, Eunice. The jacket worn by his daughter demonstrates the craft of the Catawba Cherokee in making handmade fur jackets. This type was traditionally worn with cowhide boots, and Eunice most likely wore it as a young woman. It was a family heirloom and demonstrated Native American culture in a woman's attire.

Many of Thomas's free persons of color family members were descendants of the Catawba tribe. They became ministers. One minister in the Fuller-Jackson family was Preacher Walter Jackson, his aunt Eunice Locust Fuller's husband. Walter was the Founder of Jackson Chapel, a small church located in Best Station, Wayne County, North Carolina.

Soon after Eunice and he were married, they affiliated with Thompson Chapel Holiness Church until it became a Free Will Baptist Church. They joined Rosetta and became members of Saint Delight Church in Parkstown. Vera and Luby joined Mount Zion Seventh-day Adventist Church in Parkstown in 1913.

The Fuller-Jackson family cared deeply about their connection with God. Most of them lived in and worked in the Wayne and Lenoir County communities. Thomas' son, the Reverend Lemuel H. Fuller, made his home in Chadbourn, Columbus County, North Carolina. Three of Thomas' sons tried living up North for a while, but only two remained there.

Thomas's sister Eunice preceded him in death in 1923. She died in Parkstown in a house that no longer exists and is interned in Old Mill Cemetery near Goldsboro. There are many family members buried there, including Eunice's children Luby, Ida, and Vera. Daniel is buried in Old Mill Cemetery. His daughter Rosetta, her husband Robie, and two of their children, Chester and Wilhelmina. There are over one hundred seventy people buried in this Cemetery.

African Americans would no longer be forced burial outside the Anglo cemeteries on the farms tied to their ancestor's enslavement. Choosing their burial ground solidified their new independence. They resisted placement in the separate slave burial grounds of the past. Many of the "slave" cemeteries did not have headstones, several were vandalized, and others were destroyed after the Civil War. When families were previously buried on their farms and the farms sold, the new owners would frequently turn over the ground and plant crops over the graves until that practice became forbidden.

The African American families desired marked graves since many were forbidden burial in Anglo-American cemeteries due to segregation. Therefore, Thomas' LaGrange-Goldsboro family established Old Mill as their cemetery. Nowadays, cemeteries are sacred, and there are laws in North Carolina forbidding the desecration of graves.

Though many family members migrated North and West, some wanted to return for burial, where they still called home. In Old Mill cemetery, their children could come and visit their ancestors' gravesites. A few family members did choose to be buried up North because the sting of the mistreatment they suffered in North Carolina still lingered with them. They were not willing to return to a place that they believed was horrid in life, even in their death.

Thomas permanently rests in Kinston, LaGrange, North Carolina, along with most of his children. His sisters, Eunice and Jane, and his brother, Richard, were descendants of Free People of Color. They lived in Lenoir, Nash, Robeson, Edgecombe, Cumberland, and Chatham Counties in North Carolina and Surry and Charles City County, Virginia. Typically, they owned family lands where they buried their dead. There were many cemeteries where Thomas's ancestors rest and over 162 Lumbee cemeteries in Robeson County, North Carolina.

Many Fullers, Jacksons, Parks, Artis, and Bests left North Carolina. They relocated to the northern cities of Philly and Camden. Then they spread out to Glassboro and other Cities in Camden County, New Jersey. Relocations continued to Baltimore, Maryland, and Delaware during the great migration of the 1920s to the 1950s. Moses Locust and the Roberts family relocated to Indiana, Ohio, Arkansas, Texas, and Tennessee as early as 1825.

The younger group wanted to escape bad memories and the social and racial subjugation of the South. They decided that they no longer wanted regulation to drinking out of "labeled" water fountains. They did want to wait in the back of the line in department stores or be denied food at restaurants. They wanted job opportunities other than those relegated to servitude. They sought advancement and no longer wanted subjection to the abusive behavior perpetrated against them. These restrictive conditions affected them emotionally and provided further motivation for leaving North Carolina. They additionally decided that they no longer wanted to suffer during "The Depression" in the South.

One of their parents' stories told the children of the south's living conditions had to do with their clothing. The children listened to information about the dresses that the women wore. They were made of coarse, scratchy burlap bags and nicknamed "Hoover Sacks," given this name because they were homemade garments created by the family's women. The dresses, designed from the feedbags used on the farms, were extremely unattractive and uncomfortable. Their ancestors told them that they named them after President Herbert Hoover, who was in office from 1929 to 1933. Many blamed this President for the depressed economy and the stock market crash of 1929.

Farming no longer produced enough money to feed the African American families in the 1920s. This generation was bored with the old ways. They were fed up with the abuse and no longer wanted to turn the other cheek. They wanted to be free to go where they wanted and do what they wanted. They tried to make their fortune up North.

They traveled north to be with their relatives, who told stories of good jobs in the factories and how they could make a decent wage and live better than they did in the South. The older generation moved North first and rented houses and allowed other family members to move in with them until they could find jobs and homes of their own.

Many family members went North, but some of them went West, as well. Those that went West traveled there to seek a better life during the same period as their relatives. Daniel and Florence went to Texas as migrant farmers for a while but returned to North Carolina. Ida remained in North Carolina when her brother and sister went West. Jesse and Will stayed out West, while Vera and Luby returned to North Carolina and stayed near their sister Ida and Daniel's families. James Robert Herring was the informant on her death certificate, though he continued to live in Illinois.

Thomas's cousin, Rosetta Jackson Herring, returned to North Carolina from Chicago, Illinois. She died April 12, 1946, and was interned in Newland, Pasquotank, North Carolina.

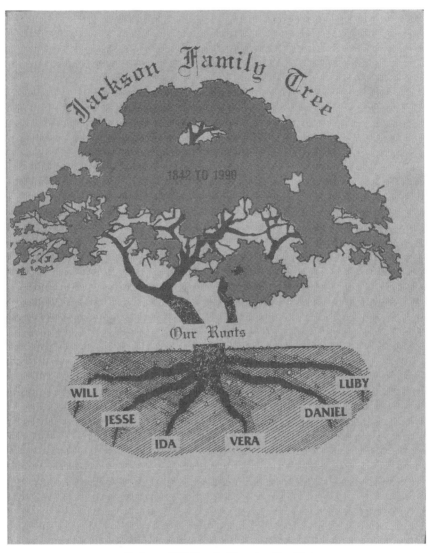

*Jackson 1990 Family Reunion Booklet.*
*Designed by the Jackson Family Reunion Committee*

Rosetta Fuller Best and her cousin, Samuel Jackson, were among the founding members of the first Jackson Family Reunion. The reunion began because the Jackson family members wanted to bring their family back together from different parts of the country. The reunion, established around 1970, brought these relatives back home for a weekend. Family members, who traveled such great distances away from their ancestral homes, welcomed the journey back to Parkstown.

The Jackson family's large reunion eventually brought over seven hundred family members together from over the United States. Many members of the family were military veterans, like Thomas. At the time of the publication of one of the Parkstown Herald Newsletters, most of these veterans' names received the honor in print. The Civil War soldiers did not receive recognition or were previously honored because their descendants did not know their names or service.

In 1988, the Goldsboro newspaper printed an article about the Jackson Family Reunion. It was the 18th Annual Reunion of the descendants of Eunice Fuller Jackson and Thomas Locust Fuller. Families expected to arrive in Goldsboro that weekend. About 700 people from 19 states, the District of Columbia, and two foreign countries in attendance. The celebration featured many activities scheduled for Saturday and Sunday.

The planned reunion program began on Friday evening with an old-fashioned backyard fish fry, complete with coleslaw and hush puppies. Saturday at 11 AM, there was a service at Mount Zion Seventh-day Adventist church. (On alternate years, the church service was on Sunday at Saint Delight Holiness Church.) Benjamin Johnson was the organist for the mass choir. The other activities that day included a fashion show and talent show at 7:30 PM at the Hermann Park Center.

A picnic at the Eastern Wayne High School cafeteria was the highlight of the Sunday program. Many of the reunion participants received colorful T-shirts featuring an emblem of the family tree. Reunion participants came from all over North Carolina, South Carolina, Florida, Georgia, Illinois, Virginia, Maryland, New Jersey, New York, Massachusetts, Tennessee, Pennsylvania, Arkansas, Missouri, California, Kansas, Colorado, Michigan, Washington, DC, New Hampshire, Canada, and Germany, according to Samuel Jackson of Parkstown, one of the planners of the event and the great-grandson of Eunice Fuller Jackson.

The family held the reunion on August 20 and 21, 1986. Local families brought desserts each year. A softball game at the local high school followed the picnic. The annual reunions began in 1970 when the Jackson family tree was traced back to 1842. It has been traced back farther to 1646, with the first female ancestor indentured in Charles City County, Virginia.

Since the family did not live close to Thomas's direct descendants, it took quite a while for the committee members to reconnect with Thomas's great-grandchildren. His grandson, Albert George Fuller, son of Thomas Fuller Jr., found his lost family. He began attending the yearly family reunions. Albert's son, James Fuller, joined with his family after his father passed away and rebuilt the strong family bonds.

Thomas Locust Fuller and his son Daniel both passed away before the family reunions began that honored them. Thomas noted Daniel's birth in the affidavit, submitted to the Army, and it clarified the incidents surrounding his birth:

Thomas submitted the document to the Department of the Military, General Affidavit, State of North Carolina, County of Lenoir, in Mrs. Beady Fuller, W. O. (Wife of) #172-9293, wife of veteran Thomas Fuller.

"On this first day of July 8, A.D. 1933, personally appeared before me and administered oaths a Notary Republic and for the "aforesaid" County and State duly authorized and administered a host that Julia Outlaw, age 70 years a resident of LaGrange, North Carolina, whose post office address is LaGrange, is well known to me and to be reputable and entitled to "credit," and who "being duly sworn, declares about the "aforesaid case" as follows:"

"I, Julia Outlaw, do hereby certify and affirm that Minerva Fuller is dead. I do not remember her death date, as death records were not kept in those days. Minerva died, leaving a baby about one day old. I was living nearby and nursed this baby from my breasts for a while. I do not know my exact age, but I guess it to be about 70 years. I know that I was the mother at that time of two children and nursed Minerva Fuller's boy after her death. "

Received (Feb. 3, 1933, Mail Sub-div., Vets. ADM. Pension). Note: Affiants should state how they gain knowledge of the facts, which they further declare that no interests and said case signed:

Witness H. L. Fuller, signed July 1, 1933.

Julia Outlaw, her (X) mark. State of North Carolina, County of Lenoir. Sworn to and subscribed before me this day by the above named Affiant.

"I certify that I read the Affidavit to say, Affiant, including the words JULIA OUTLAW erased and JULIA OUTLAW, added. In addition, acquainted with its contents before I executed the same, I further state that I am in nowise interested in said case, nor I am concerned in its prosecution, and that said Affiant I have personally known to me, and she is a credible person."

Witness my hand and seal of office this one 1ˢᵗ day of JULY 1933. E. B. Reagan, Notary Republic. My service expires December 1, 1933 post office address is LaGrange, N. C. Additional evidence claim of Beatty Fuller affidavit of JULIA OUTLAW, LaGrange, North Carolina, age 70. Filed by John J. O'Brien, Attorney for Claimant. Vicar Building, Washington DC.

Note: to be executed before some officer authorized to administer oaths for general purposes—the official character and signature of any such officer not required by law to use.

The clerk of the proper court, giving dates of beginning and close of the official term, must certify a seal. If such certificate is on file, so state."

Julia Outlaw's maiden name was Locust, and her father was Richard Locust, born in 1822 and Thomas' great uncle. The Locust name generally was spelled differently on many court and census documents.

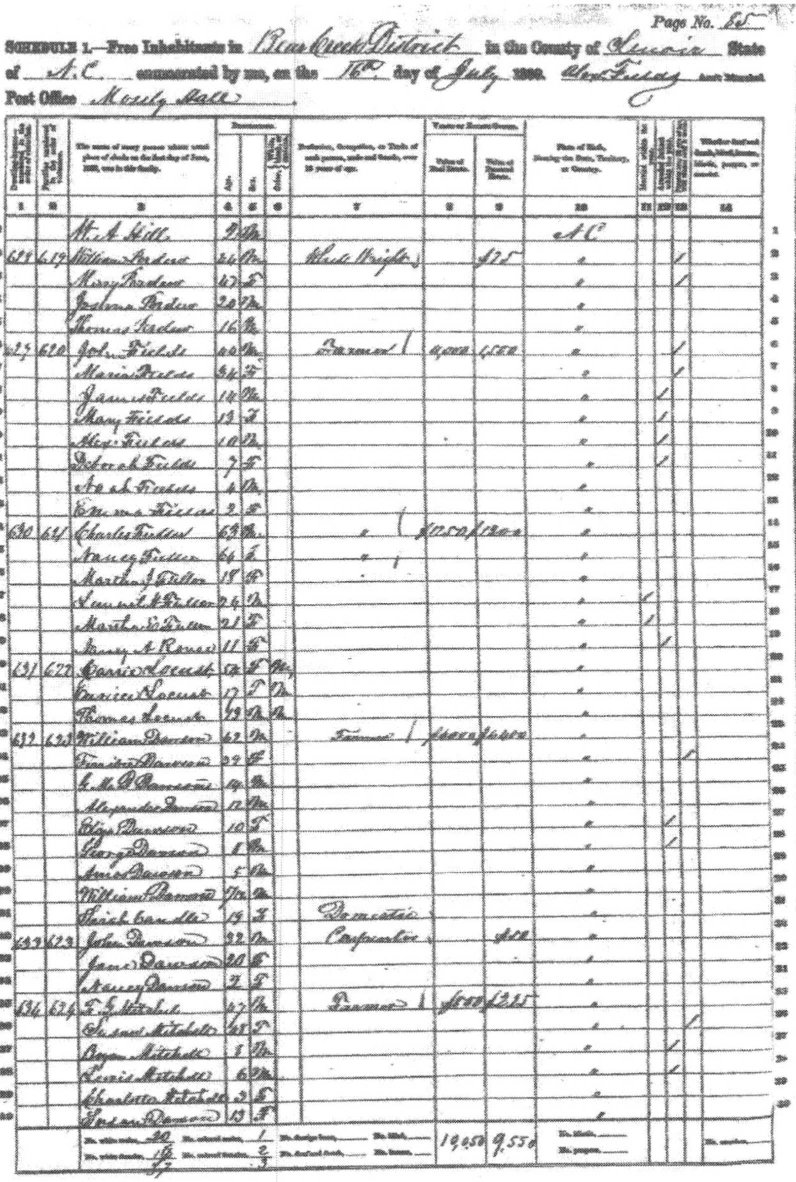

Page No. 85

SCHEDULE 1.—Free Inhabitants in Bear Creek District in the County of Lenoir State of N.C. enumerated by me, on the 16th day of July 1860. Post Office Mosely Hall

| | | | | | | | | | |
|---|---|---|---|---|---|---|---|---|---|
| | | W. A. Hill | 9 | M | | | | | N.C. |
| 629 | 619 | William Radford | 44 | M | | Wheelwright | | 175 | " |
| | | Mary Radford | 47 | F | | | | | " |
| | | Joshua Radford | 20 | M | | | | | " |
| | | Thomas Radford | 16 | M | | | | | " |
| 627 | 620 | John Fields | 40 | M | | Farmer | 4000 | 4500 | " |
| | | Maria Fields | 34 | F | | | | | " |
| | | James Fields | 14 | M | | | | | " |
| | | Mary Fields | 13 | F | | | | | " |
| | | Alex Fields | 10 | M | | | | | " |
| | | Deborah Fields | 7 | F | | | | | " |
| | | Noah Fields | 4 | M | | | | | " |
| | | Emma Fields | 2 | F | | | | | " |
| 630 | 621 | Charles Fields | 63 | M | | " | [illegible] | [illegible] | " |
| | | Nancy Fields | 64 | F | | | | | " |
| | | Martha J Fields | 18 | F | | | | | " |
| | | Samuel Fields | 24 | M | | | | | " |
| | | Martha Fields | 21 | F | | | | | " |
| | | Mary A Rouse | 11 | F | | | | | " |
| 631 | 622 | Caroline Locust | 52 | F | Mu | | | | " |
| | | Eunice Locust | 17 | F | Mu | | | | " |
| | | Thomas Locust | 49 | M | Mu | | | | " |
| 632 | 623 | William Dawson | 62 | M | | Farmer | [illegible] | [illegible] | " |
| 633 | 623 | John Dawson | 32 | M | | Carpenter | | [illegible] | " |
| 634 | 624 | [illegible] Mitchell | 47 | M | | Farmer | [illegible] | [illegible] | " |

*1860 U.S. Census with Caroline, Eunice and Thomas Locust living in Bear Creek, Lenoir, North Carolina, U.S. Census Bureau, Washington, D.C.*

Julia's father, Richard, was very close to his family, and his daughter married a man named Wright Outlaw. She and her husband, Wright, were living next door to her father, Richard, and her mother,

Elizabeth Betsy Evans Locust, on the 1870 census in Nash County, North Carolina.

While they were living in Nash County, Daniel was born four years later. Julia stepped in to help her cousin, Thomas, as has been the custom in their family. When needed, women in the family always stepped in and helped with estranged or orphaned children. When family members traveled for work, had children, were alone, or the parents passed away, they could depend on their relatives to step up and help raise the children. The Locust family lived by the African proverb and knew it indeed "took a village to raise a child." The Lucas-Fuller-Jackson family raised quite a few.

# CHAPTER 5

## Thomas's Military Life and Struggles

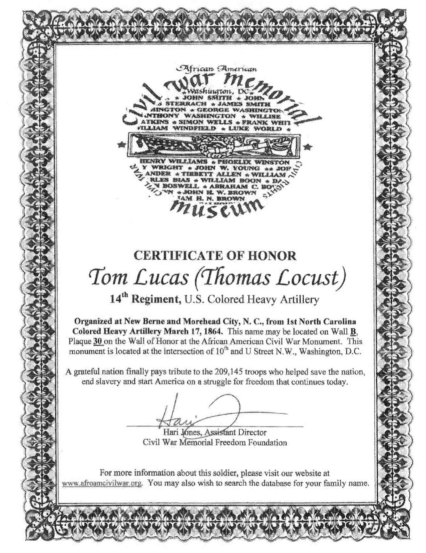

African American

Civil War Memorial Museum

Washington, DC

* JOHN SMITH * JOHN
* STERRACH * JAMES SMITH
HINGTON * GEORGE WASHINGTON
NTHONY WASHINGTON * WILLISE
ATKINS * SIMON WELLS * FRANK WHIT
VILLIAM WINDFIELD * LUKE WORLD *

HENRY WILLIAMS * PHORLIX WINSTON
Y WRIGHT * JOHN W. YOUNG ** JOP
ANDER * TIBBETT ALLEN * WILLIAM
RLES BIAS * WILLIAM BOON * D/
N BOSWELL * ABRAHAM C. BO
N * JOHN H. W. BROWN
AM H. N. BROWN

### CERTIFICATE OF HONOR

## *Tom Lucas (Thomas Locust)*
14th Regiment, U.S. Colored Heavy Artillery

**Organized at New Berne and Morehead City, N. C., from 1st North Carolina Colored Heavy Artillery March 17, 1864.** This name may be located on Wall **B**, Plaque **30** on the Wall of Honor at the African American Civil War Monument. This monument is located at the intersection of 10th and U Street N.W., Washington, D.C.

A grateful nation finally pays tribute to the 209,145 troops who helped save the nation, end slavery and start America on a struggle for freedom that continues today.

Hari Jones, Assistant Director
Civil War Memorial Freedom Foundation

For more information about this soldier, please visit our website at www.afroamcivilwar.org. You may also wish to search the database for your family name.

*Courtesy African American Civil War Memorial Museum, Washington, D.C.*

When Thomas first enlisted in the military, he enlisted in New Bern, North Carolina, on his birthday, April 21, 1865, for a three-year

72

term. At that time, he did not know when the war would end; he only knew that the fighting had already lasted three years. The Army Captain wanted to know how tall Thomas was, his complexion, birth date, and other pertinent information at the recruitment office.

Thomas enlisted in the Union Army much later than his uncle Richard did. His uncle enlisted in the Civil War. As soon as Thomas became aware of the battles and saw the recruitment posters, he was very eager to join the Union troops. Thomas was forced to wait until he was eighteen years old to join the military. He wanted to enlist earlier but could not due to the age requirement.

When relatives, friends, and neighbors were enlisting to fight in the Civil War, he wanted to join them. Though he was already "Free," he was very motivated. He knew what conditions were like for other free and enslaved persons of color in his community. Thomas wanted to participate in the battle, and his age did not deter him. He knew that his enlistment could help his family.

Although Thomas enlisted at New Bern, he mustered in at Morehead City, North Carolina. He received a bounty of $300.00 upon enlistment. Thomas received his assignment to Fort Macon military base in North Carolina. He arrived at Morehead City upon the Atlantic and North Carolina Railroad on the day of his muster.

The First Regiment, Heavy Artillery, (African Descent) 14th U. S. Colored Troops organized at New Bern and Morehead City, North Carolina, March 1864. The Companies mustered between February 4, 1864, and April 30, 1865. Their designation changed to the 14th U.S. Colored Heavy Artillery on March 17, 1865. "L" Company mustered out on December 11, 1865, at Ft. Macon, North Carolina. After his service, Thomas traveled around for a few years before returning to Lenoir County.

Along with Thomas Company, soldiers assigned to Company L mustered in at Morehead city from March 28 through April 24, 1865. Fort Macon was a five-sided fort located by the water near Atlantic Beach, North Carolina. There were many men stationed there. The highest number of troops reached 883 soldiers of Anglo, African, and Native American descent.

Thomas was a Private, though his comrade, Isaac Applewhite, was promoted to Corporal within two weeks after arriving on Station. Both men served under an Anglo-American commander, which was generally a common practice. Soldiers of African Descent, relegated to the lowest ranks, continued volunteering after the war ended.

The Louisiana Native Guard was an exception to the typical rank structure for Colored Troops. Their initial volunteers were "Free Men of Color," as was Thomas. The first Louisiana Native Guard was one of the first exclusively African American Regiments to fight in the Union Army. They originated in New Orleans, Louisiana, in 1862, which occurred during the same period of the "Siege of Fort Macon." The Native Guard had 1,000 soldiers when they organized.

The unit had Line officers who were Lieutenants and Captains, although higher-ranking officers were still Anglo. Their fellow Anglo Union soldiers treated them so poorly that a large group of African American officers resigned. Most of the enlisted men just deserted. The Army dissolved this Unit in April 1864. The Army subsequently placed the one who remained in the newly organized 73rd and 74th Regiments of the United States Colored Troops. By the end of the Civil War, only 100 of 1,000 original Native Guard enlistees remained.

Fort Macon consisted of a large military compound constructed of brick and mortar that faced the water. The soldiers climbed the high stairs to overlook the water and had a clear vision for miles to see the enemy approaching. These soldiers were able to fire their cannons from various positions along the two-story wall. The Fort provided safety to the men in case the opposing troops came by sea.

The Anglo officers had small cottages that were mainly constructed of wood within the Fort and no longer exist. These cottages were drafty and often required repair. Some of the Anglo officer's families lived with them after the war was over.

The barracks consisted of large rooms within the outer brick walls, and it was where the soldiers slept. There could be as many as 70-80 men per room. The soldiers slept two persons per bunk, facing head to foot. It was not a comfortable sleeping arrangement, and they were too crowded. The men took shifts sleeping, and some slept while the others were on guard or working.

The mattresses, made of straw, subjected the soldiers to a bedbug epidemic. The soldiers stripped the beds once a week. Every Saturday, they washed everything down with Lime and Carbolic Acid to get rid of the bedbugs. They also washed down the walls and floors weekly. The soldiers added fresh straw to the bunks each week. Fort Macon continually suffered a problem with bedbugs. When they discovered DDT, they began using it and controlled the infestations.

The men wore woolen uniforms, both summer and winter. The soldiers wore linen underwear and shirts. The only heat source they had was fireplaces in each room. The brick walls kept the temperature cooler in the summer, but the buildings were drafty and cold in the winter.

Thomas's duty was a yard servant. He took his job seriously and cleaned everything in the yard and on the grounds. He was also responsible for maintaining the yards around the officers' cottages. Since he was a farmer, he was comfortable tending plants and vegetables and cleaning the yard.

Several units were assigned to Fort Macon between April 1865 and December 1865, during the Reconstruction Era. The Units stationed at Fort Macon organized at New Bern and Morehead City, North Carolina, as the 1st North Carolina Colored Heavy Artillery March 14 or 17, 1864 - April 30, 1865.

From June 1865 to August 1865, the units stationed at Fort Macon were the 14th U.S. Colored Heavy Artillery Companies H, I, L, and M. Units. From August 1865 until September 1865 also included Thomas Fuller's unit, the 14th U.S.

*Thomas Fuller's NARA Service Record. National Archives, Washington, D.C.*

Heavy Artillery. All companies were located there from September 1865 to October 1865.

.

The 14th U.S. Colored Heavy Artillery Companies A, D, E, G, and H were there. The Units Companies A, B, C, D, E, F, G, H, I, K, L, and M mustered out on December 11, 1865. From November 1865 to December 1865, the 14th U.S. Colored Heavy Artillery was part of the last volunteer Army soldiers released from military duty.

Thomas was located at Fort Macon from April until December; therefore, L Company at Fort Macon during the early Reconstruction Era. When the war ended, the Union Army dismissed the volunteer troops, and they returned home. Since there was no longer a need for volunteers, Fort Macon was manned by the regular Army. The Fort was just maintaining and handling any problems that arose during Reconstruction.

*Entrance of Ft. Macon, North Carolina*
*Photographed by S.R.*

New Bern had a sizeable military recruitment center, and at one time, they had 35,000 Union Soldiers located there. The Center suffered severe overcrowding, and many soldiers became sick with diseases and infections from mosquitoes, ticks, and bedbugs.

Thomas first applied for an Invalid Pension on May 22, 1892, in Thomas Lucas's name. He attempted it again on September 16, 1908, and the Army rejected it. When he was sixty years old and in poor health, his doctor said he had asthma and heart disease. Still, the army determined that there was "no notable degree of disability found."

*Fort Macon Cannon, Fort Macon State Park, N.C.*
*Photographed by S.R.*

To receive his pension, Thomas completed numerous documents. This particular document was a form that Thomas himself dictated, and it provides a look into his life.

Department of the Interior, Southern Division, Invoice Original # 1189.622, Thomas Lucas, Company L. 14, Reg't U.S.C.H.A., Bureau of Pensions, Washington, D.C., May 16, 1902.

Sir: to aid this Bureau in preventing anyone falsely personating you, or otherwise committing fraud in your name, or because of your service, you are required to answer the enumerated questions fully. You will please return this circular under cover of the enclosed envelope, which requires no postage.

Thomas's son, Hardy, completed the document and returned it to the Army under their cover.

Thomas Lucas, Fountain Hill, Greene County, North Carolina, D.T. Ware, Commissioner.

1. Where were you born?   Answer: "At La Grange, N.C."

2. Where did you enlist?     Answer: "At New Bern, N.C."

3. Where had you lived before you enlisted? Answer: "Lenoir County."

4. What was your occupation? Answer: "I was a yard servant."

5. Were you a slave? If so, state the names of all former owners and particularly the name of your owner at the date of your enlistment: Answer: "**I was Free Born**."

6. Where were you discharged? Answer "at Ft. Macon."

7. Where have you lived since discharge? Give dates, as nearly as possible, of any changes in residence.: "I've only been a citizen of Lenoir County."

8. What is your present occupation? Answer. "Farming"

9. What is your height? Answer: "Five feet, eight inches." What color of your skin? "Brown." Are there any permanent marks or scars on your person? If so, describe them? "No."

10. Were you in the military or naval service under a name different from that by which now known? If so, state what it was.: "I was known as Thomas Lucas."

11. Have you ever been known by any names other than that given in your application for a pension? If so, state them in full. "Thomas Fuller."

12. By what name are you now known? State it in full. "Thomas Fuller."

13. What is your actual residence at the present time, and what is your nearest post office? "Fountain Hill, Greene County, N.C."

Dated: June 2, 1902.

Very respectfully,

Hardy Lincoln Fuller

The document shows that Thomas Lucas was a Free Man of Color when he enlisted in the military.

The 1850 U.S. Census shows Thomas and his sisters, Eunice and Cathy Jane, as Mulatto in their mother's home. Thomas was two years old, proving he was born in 1847; additionally, this census verifies the family's "Free" status. On that Census, his mother, Caroline, was listed as household head and as Mulatto. She was a "Free Woman of Color."

Locust family names appeared on both the 1850 and 1860 U.S. Census, so they were obviously "Free." Enslaved people appeared listed by age and color on separate slave schedules under the name of the enslaver. These unfortunate enslaved persons did not individually have their names listed because they were not considered citizens but the enslaver's property.

Many of the African American Union Soldiers did not enlist under their fathers' names. If they were not previously free, under their enslavers, they might not have a surname. Since these name changes were a common practice, the U.S. Pension Office had to ensure that the person applying for the Civil War pension was the same person who served.

Therefore, to receive his pension Thomas had to seek friends and relatives who were very familiar with him and could complete affidavits on his behalf. Two of Thomas Locust's military comrades submitted another affidavit.

This Affidavit submitted in support of Thomas Locust Fuller's request for military pension:

General Affidavit, State of North Carolina, County of Lenoir, in the matter of Thomas Fuller alias Thomas Lucas L. 14, USCHA on this 5th day of July, JC SC Cox, Notary Republic, and for that and for said County duly authorized to administer oaths:

ISAAC APPLEWHITE, age 58 years, resident of Lenoir, in the County of Lenoir, and State of North Carolina, whose post office address is LaGrange Station and ELLIS JACKSON, aged 58 years, a resident of Lenoir, and the County of Lenoir in the State of North Carolina, whose post office address is Kinston, and well-known to be reputable and entitled to the credit, and who being duly sworn, declared in relation to aforesaid case as follows:

"That we were well acquainted with Thomas Fuller while he was in the USA and Company L, 14th Regiment of Heavy Artillery and was comrades with him and that he is the identical person whose name was then Thomas Lucas, and when he joined the Army he gave his mother's name, and after he was discharged from the Army he changed his name to Fuller as his father was named PETER FULLER. ISAAC APPLEWHITE and ELLIS JACKSON further make an affidavit that he has been personally acquainted with Thomas Fuller for over 50 years. We further declare that we have no interest in said case, and we are not concerned in its prosecution.

With the contents before they executed the same, I further certify that I am nowise interested in said case, nor am I concerned in its prosecution and other after yet personally known to me that they are credible persons."
Witnesses: J.G. COX and HARDY L. FULLER

Affiants: Isaac (his mark) Applewhite and Ellis Jackson.
JG Cox, Notary Republic, this is affidavit number 1189662.

ADDITIONAL EVIDENCE. The claim of Thomas Fuller alias Thomas Lucas, joint AFFIDAVIT of Isaac Applewhite and Ellis Jackson. Filed by W. H. WILLS, Attorney at Law, Wills Building, 312 Indiana Avenue, Washington, DC.

Thomas's comrade, Isaac Applewhite's wife, also applied for a pension. Isaac's application was separate from Thomas's application. Isaac enlisted in the Union Army in Morehead City, North Carolina. In Wayne County, North Carolina, he was not free but enslaved by a farmer named Elisha Applewhite. He was also 18 years old at the time of his enlistment.

In Isaac's pension application, he stated that he was born in Wayne County, North Carolina. He said that he was a Corporal in the Company L, 14$^{th}$ Regiment Heavy Artillery. On August 16, 1912, he stated that he was a farmer and described himself as 5 feet, 9 inches tall, and dark-complexioned, and he had one scar on his right hip. He received this scar when hurt by a barrel of flour, which fell on him.

Isaac enlisted on April 18, 1865, and came from Goldsboro, North Carolina. He mustered in the Army in Morehead City, North Carolina. Isaac's enlistment roll shows that his wife applied for his pension on March 11, 1919.

The letter reads,

"Dear Sir, in reference to Sarah Applewhite, widow of Isaac Applewhite, who was a Cpl. Company L, 14th Regiment, United States Colored Heavy Artillery, Certificate dated March 11, 1919. Husband, Isaac Applewhite, who died in August 1917.

*Thomas' Pension Document Listing His Nine Children and his First Wife, Minerva.*

This is a worthy old lady. I trust her pension can be put through all right. I enclose you here with the necessary papers as we think to get her on the pension roll. It has taken considerable time to get up these papers. If there are any further affidavits, please advise us. We will try to get them.

We have no interest whatsoever in this pension. We only want to help the old lady.

Yours Truly,

J. T. Heath

Sarah Applewhite
Kinston, North Carolina RR1.

This was the response to Sarah's request for a Widows' Pension:

The Department of the Interior, Bureau of Pensions, Washington.

Your communication on the number # 3 instruction informs this Bureau of Isaac Applewhite's death, a pensioner by certificate number 113-9206, without giving the date.

You will confer a favor by stating the date of the pensioner's death. If not ascertainable by you note on the bottom fold of this letter and return the same under cover of the enclosed penalty envelope, it requires no postage. Very respectfully, E. C. Fieman, Acting Commissioner.

[Enclosure]

Lenoir County, North Carolina

Isaac Applewhite died on August 15, 1917. Sarah (her X Mark) Applewhite

Witness J. T. Heath

*Thomas' Pension Approval in 1912 and Disbursements.*
*National Archives Washington, DC.*

August 3, 1917

Clerk Superior Court for North Carolina.

Another affidavit submitted by Richard Locust Jr., son of Richard Locust Sr. and Susan Easter Minton (later Tilghman), who was Caroline's grandson and raised him:

The following: "General Affidavit, State of North Carolina, County of Lenoir. In the matter of

"Mrs. Beady Fuller, the widow of Thomas Fuller, served under the name, Thomas Lucas, Company L, 14$^{th}$ Heavy Arty. On this 1$^{st}$ day of February AD., 1933, personally appeared before me, a Notary Republic in and for the County above and State, duly authorized to administer oaths, RICHARD LOCUST, age 66 years, a resident of Lenoir County, North Carolina. P.O. Box Kinston, whose post office address is R. F. D. # 2, Kinston. NC. Well, known to me to be reputably entitled to a credit, and who being duly sworn declares his relation to the aforesaid case as follows:

"I have known Thomas Fuller all my life. I know that he was the husband of Minerva Dawson Fuller. I lived in the family with them, and I was present when she died. I attended the burial but do not remember the date of her death.

I know when the said Thomas Fuller married his second wife, Beady Coward. I have lived around and about them all through their married life, except for 1890 – 1891. I lived in Tennessee, and in 1892 I moved back to this state and located near the said Thomas Fuller and found him and his wife Beady living together and lived together until the date of his death, and they were never divorced."

(Note – Affiants should state how they gained knowledge of the facts which they testify.) He further declares that he has no interest in said case, and I'm not concerned in its prosecution. Witness: H. L. Fuller, Kinston, N.C. E. O. B. Douglass, Kinston, N.C., if affiant sign by Mark two witnesses who can write.

Received February 2, 1930, Mail SUB-DIV. Vets Admin Pension, #3 State of North Carolina County of Lenoir. SWORN to and subscribed before me this day by the above-named affiant …. and I certify I read said affidavit to said affiant, including the words divorced erased. The words divorced, added, and acquainted with him with its contents, I executed the same.

I further certify that I am now interested in the said case, nor am I concerned about its prosecution. The affiant is personally known to me and is a credible person:

WITNESS MY HAND AND SEAL OF OFFICE this 1st day of February 1933. J. W. Fitzpatrick Notary Public, my commission expires January 18, 1934. Post Office Address is…LaGrange, N.C.

NOTE … to be executed before some officer authorized to administer oaths for general purposes. The clerk of the proper court, giving dates of beginning and close of the official term, must certify any such officer's official character and signature not required by law to use a seal. If such certificate is on file, so state.

Thomas's doctor stated that his military service caused his rheumatism. Thomas's family sent documents many times concerning his health, and as he aged, his health continued to deteriorate. His doctor submitted a paper on March 30, 1908, and it said:

"He is a practicing physician and has known the soldier mentioned earlier for about three years and that "I've been his medical advisor since I have known him. He had asthma and chronic rheumatism, and some organic heart trouble when he first came to see me in 1905. He has continuously visited me for medical aid ever since.

When I first consulted him, he could hardly be of one-third 1/3 service in his usual occupation. His rheumatism is confined to the lumbar region of his back. He is gradually growing woozy and is not so …? off now and one-half ½. As he stated, I am fully persuading to believe that extreme exposure during military services in the war of 1865 was the …? beginning of his present physical disabilities."

Thomas's doctor stated: "His family history was exceptionally good, both mother and father living to old age and never suffered from any of the troubles he now suffers." Thomas' father, Peter, lived well into his late seventies, reaching the age of seventy-seven. His mother, Caroline, lived to eighty-six years old.

It took twenty years from Thomas's initial application in 1892 until his pension approval on July 15, 1912; the Army approved for $13.50 a month. On April 21, 1913, his pension increased to $15.50 a month. On April 21, 1917, Thomas's allotment grew to $19.00 a month.

His pension increased again in 1922 to $22.50 per month; then, it grew to $30.00 a month in 1918. By 1919, his assistance had risen to $32.00 a month.

On October 8, 1924, Thomas sent in an additional Declaration for Pension under Thomas Fuller's name with his alias referenced. The Pension Department incorrectly listed Thomas's occupation as "Slave," demonstrating that they did not review his previous documents. They believed that every African American soldier was enslaved before the Civil War.

In this document, Thomas was seventy years old. He suffered from partial blindness, heart trouble, weak nerves, stiff joints due to rheumatic disorder, continual cold feet. Simultaneously, all other parts of his body stayed in a moist sweat, cataract of the eyes, and loss of all teeth.

Thomas spent a great deal of time outside in the cold weather while he was in the military, which caused him to have physical problems. Though he suffered many ailments, he lived longer than his two best comrades did. His friend, Isaac Applewhite, died in 1917 at the age of sixty-nine years old.

William Henry Warters of Lenoir County, NC, enslaved Ellis Warters Jackson. Ellis entered the military under the surname Warters. When released from the military, he gained his freedom like many other soldiers who survived the war. An affidavit was submitted and included in his pension files was from his enslaver's son, John T. Warters. John stated that his father, who passed away in 1862, had given Ellis the Warters surname.

*1915 Affidavit from Hardy Fuller, Attesting to His Father, Thomas'*
*Physical Condition for Pension. National Archives, Washington, D.C.*

Additional information that Ellis Jackson received from his mother in 1866 was his actual date of birth. When he entered the military, he thought that he had been born in 1848 since that was the information provided him by William Warters. He then offered this information to the Army upon his enlistment because he believed it to be correct. His mother told him that he was born on June 5, 1846.

In Ellis's application for his pension, he explained the reason for his name change. He spoke with his mother, and she told him that he should use the Jackson surname because his father was named Moses Jackson. Ellis changed his name to Jackson as soon as he was able. He was granted his pension and married his sweetheart, Priscilla Warters, in November 1870, and they raised several children.

Priscilla passed away in 1892. Ellis then married Penny Miller in March 1901, and she died in August 1914, but he said that they had separated for about eight years before she died. Penny was first married to Ellis Becton. They divorced in 1889, and Ellis Jackson responded to the military when asked what organizations Ellis Becton had a membership. Ellis stated that he did not know of any organizations to which Ellis Becton belonged. Ellis passed away in 1926 at the age of seventy-eight years old. He was living in Lenoir County, North Carolina, when he passed away.

In many cases, African Americans changed their names when they enlisted in the Civil War. One reason was enslavement and the fact that they had run away to join the army and avoid capture. Some ran out in the night to prevent killed. These African American volunteers did not want to carry the surname of the person who held them in bondage. Many took the last name of their family before they were sold away to reconnect with them. Many ex-enslaved persons sought out their families by putting ads in the local papers and asking to find their relatives.

Fort Macon was far from Thomas's home, but he had comrades stationed with him that were his friends from Kinston, North Carolina. He was very close to Ellis Warters Jackson and Isaac Applewhite. They both acknowledged that Thomas used his mother's maiden name, Locust entered the military. Jackson and Applewhite also stated that when Thomas applied for his pension, he had changed to his father's surname, Fuller.

Thomas's case regarding his name change was slightly different from his comrades. His mother was a Free Woman of Color, and his father, Peter Fuller, was enslaved and not permitted to marry. Like many of his fellow soldiers, Thomas did not immediately return to the small cities and towns they previously lived. Some of the soldiers never returned to their wives and families; they just began new lives.

One of Thomas' comrades, Ellis Jackson, stated in his affidavit that he had known Thomas for over fifty years. Thomas's sister, Jane, had Jackson's surname. Ellis also used an alias surname, Warters, when he enlisted in the Army. He stated he was 18 years old when he enlisted in April.

When Ellis applied for his pension, he, like Thomas, used his correct surname, Jackson. Ellis took the Warters name from his future wife, Priscilla "Prissy" Warters; Ellis used her surname when he enlisted. Ellis Jackson's pension records stated that he did not marry her until 1870 after returning from the war. Ellis Jackson's father was Moses Jackson, and his mother was Eliza Jones.

In 1870 the U.S. Census showed Thomas living with his cousin Joseph Griffin and wife, Eliza, in Ward 2, Madison, Louisiana, outside of New Orleans. Though Thomas did not see battle, he was attacked. He did suffer some indignities from a fellow Anglo Union soldier when he was in Richmond, Virginia.

The Freedmen's Bureau documented this incident. They were an organization, which started a bank for previously enslaved people and helped with the resettlement of formerly enslaved African Americans. They also assisted African Americans who were free before the War Between the States. They collected narratives about the African American's experiences in slavery and while in uniform. Thomas's complaint was in one of these documents.

From the Freedmen's Bureau: "Statement of Thomas Lucas (colored) of his abuse by the Provost Marshal 12 June 1865. Thomas Lucas (colored) states that he was sitting down near Fifth and Broad Street on the sidewalk, on a store carriage step. He, suffering great pain from a toothache when a squad of soldiers had been dispersing a crowd nearby.

They ordered all to move away. "Thomas said that he was sitting on the sidewalk and got up to move, and one of the guards (in liquor) overtook him and struck him on the hip with his gun. He took his gun with both hands, using it as a club, and struck him (Lucas) in the back, hurting him severely, and from which he is now suffering great pain, and this occurred about 7:00 PM tonight."

Thomas had problems with his teeth for years. He stated that he had lost all of his teeth in his pension documents before he passed away. Besides, the blow from that gun probably caused him lifelong pain. It affected his rheumatism claim, also documented in his pension records.

Though many African Americans voluntarily enlisted, they had many obstacles against them because some Northern soldiers mistreated them. The Southern soldiers killed them upon contact and never attempted to take them as prisoners. Confederate soldiers resented African Americans for running away because of their loss of free labor. These Southerners vowed not to take the African Americans as prisoners but to kill them on the spot.

Minerva's brother, Randall Dawson, enlisted May 20, 1863, in New Bern, North Carolina. He was shot, wounded, and left on the Battlefield at the Civil War at Olustee, Florida. Randall was in the U.S. 35$^{th}$ Colored Cavalry. Less than a year after he enlisted, he was wounded and missing in action by the Army records on February 20, 1864. Like many other forgotten brave young, enslaved African American soldiers, Randall Dawson died in battle.

Many of Thomas's cousins were tradesmen, and carpenters were the most common, although his father was a blacksmith. Thomas's uncle, Isham Locus Jr., his mother's brother, was also a carpenter, moved to Belmont, Ohio, and enlisted in the Civil War there. Isham Locust Sr. was Isham Junior and Caroline's father, and Thomas' grandfather.

*Fort Macon Marker, Fort Macon State Park, N.C.*
*Photographed by S.R.*

African Americans, both free and enslaved, wanted to fight with the Union troops. Initially, the federal government and the Confederate army refused African American military volunteers. Some Free African Americans from New Orleans and South Carolina initially volunteered to assist the Confederate Army. The Union Army maltreated many African American soldiers.

Some of these soldiers believed that they were fighting for Southern States' rights but soon discovered the war's primary purpose. African American soldiers realized the Southern focus on the Civil War did not center on land rights. The fight concentrated on keeping themselves and their brothers and sisters in bondage. After they realized this, it caused the Free Men to change their stance on Southern rights. Men often enlisted in a company recruited in the counties where they lived, though not always. After several battles, companies combined because so many men were wounded or killed.

Frederick Douglass spent a significant amount of time proposing that African American enslaved men fight for the Union. He believed that military service would help the cause of racial injustice. His famous quote was, "Let the black man get upon his person the brass letters the U.S., let him get an eagle on his button and a musket on his shoulder. There is no power on earth which can deny that he earned the right to citizenship in the United States."

African American leaders sent petitions to President Abraham Lincoln, begging him to allow African soldiers to fight. They also urged him to abolish slavery to hurt Confederates by freeing their slaves. After much debate within the government, Lincoln finally decided to let African Americans serve in the military and abolish slavery in the "rebel" states. Lincoln made his announcement in September 1862, and his decision became law on January 1, 1863.

The Emancipation Proclamation freed the slaves of rebel masters. It paved the way for growing numbers of Africans to enter the Union Army. Commander Ulysses S. Grant welcomed them.

*Fort Macon Soldiers Dining Room, Fort Macon State Park, N.C.*
*Photographed by S.R*

Lincoln argued that "By arming the Negro, we have added a powerful ally. They will make good soldiers and taking them from the enemy, and we can see him in the same proportion as they strengthen us."

The Confederates announced that they would not treat African soldiers fairly. They angrily declared that any African Union uniform would be treated as insurrectionists, shot on sight, and no prisoner. This terrible threat hung over every African Union soldier.

The African American soldiers faced segregation in the Union Army as well. Anglo officers were in charge of colored troops. One officer in charge of training raw African recruits complained of constant scrutiny. He said: "I sometimes felt as if we were a plant trying to take root, but constantly pulled up to see if we were growing." In May 1863, some of the first African Union soldiers who went into combat fought at the Battle of Port Hudson near Pittsburgh, Mississippi. The New York Tribune reported on this important event.

Thomas's uncle, Richard Locust, left North Carolina in 1863 and went to Washington, DC. He stated that he was single on his draft documents and was a resident of that district when he left a wife and several children in Lenoir County, North Carolina. He did return to his wife and children after the war was over.

Richard reported his birthplace as Georgetown, District of Columbia, and drafted into the Army at thirty-three. Richard Locust was not listed on his military records by his correct surname but by the surname "Lucas." Thomas's name is also listed in his military records as Lucas and not Locust. Since these men did not know how to read or write, they could not tell the Army the proper spelling of their names.

*Fort Macon Soldiers Dining Room, Fort Macon State Park, N.C.*
*Photographed by S.R.*

## CHAPTER 6

## Civil War and Revolutionary Patriot Kin

Many of the African American soldiers ran away from the plantations to enlist in the military. They escaped because they feared retaliation from their Anglo neighbors, who might resent them for joining the Union Army. Another of Thomas' cousins was a free man of color, Nathan Lucas. Nathan was born in Pittsboro, Chatham County, North Carolina, and lived in Lenoir County, as Thomas did. Nathan enlisted in a New Orleans Regiment, Company 4, U.S. Colored Cavalry. He married Maria Brown in 1869 in New Orleans and was a carpenter like many of Thomas' other cousins.

Simon Locust, another of Thomas's cousins, was also a Free Person of Color Civil War soldier who fought for the Union army. He Mustered on October 13, 1864, as a Private in Co. E, 28th Infantry, 13th Regt. in Jeffersonville, Stampers Creek Township, Orange County, Indiana. Simon mustered out at Nashville, Tennessee, on October 18, 1865.

Simon only spent one year in the United States Colored Troops Army because he was not a volunteer like Thomas's comrades and other family members. Instead, the Union Army drafted Private Simon Locust to fight in Indiana. In contrast, his family, who lived in North Carolina, were a part of a volunteer Army. Simon lived freely in Indiana, but his North Carolina family still dealt with strict southern laws and the possibility of kidnap.

He, like many in Thomas's family, was also a minister. Reverend Simon Locust was born circa 1827 and married three times. First to Isabella Roberts on June 14, 1849, in Orange County, Indiana. Secondly, he married Patience "Polly" Horton on October 12, 1865, in North Carolina. Then he married Florence Stewart on December 12, 1885, in Orange County, Indiana.

Reverend Simon Locust was the son of North Carolina parents Moses Locust and Ferebee Locust. Moses moved his family to Orange County, Indiana, from North Carolina around 1820.

Simon's mother was Valentine Locust's daughter. Her siblings Polly and Absolom were kidnapped as young children in Wake County, North Carolina. Rachel Pettiford Locust was Farabee's mother.

Valentine and Rachel's children escaped their captors and eventually returned to their parents. Ferebee's brother, Absalom Locust and, sister, Polly Locust, were stolen from their parents in 1801 in Raleigh, North Carolina. The child stealers felt it was easier to capture children and sell them into slavery because they would not typically have "Free Papers."

Once the Melungeon families moved to Indiana, the descendants of the Roberts, Archers, and Locusts found themselves in a place where they could build a new life and have land of their own. Many Free People of Color traveled to Indiana with the Quakers. They built communities in Indiana and Ohio, but as they began to have more children, the land parcels became smaller and smaller. The shrinkage of land ownership was due to repartitioning with each new generation.

Eventually, these smaller land parcels make it more challenging to support a family. Most of the families depended on the land because they were farmers as their ancestors had been. As their land began to dry up and the crops died, the North Carolina transplants had little desire to stay there. Somewhere around the 1850s, before the Civil War, these Melungeon families began moving again because their Anglo neighbors at Lick Creek, Indiana, and Lost Creek, Ohio, were harassing them. They decided to find better land opportunities elsewhere.

Reverend Simon Locust was born in Lick Creek, Orange County, Indiana, in 1824. He must have returned to North Carolina to marry his second wife, Polly Horton, since their registered marriage record was on file in North Carolina. The families abandoned the Lick Creek Cemetery, and Simon was the last person to be buried there in 1891. Some of the family moved to Belmont, Ohio, and eventually to Nova Scotia, Canada. Some returned to North Carolina after the Civil War.

A monument, erected by the Boy Scouts, previously stood at Lick Creek Community, Orange County, Indiana. The State Park removed the memorial due to inaccurate inscriptions. The monument listed Simon Locust as a Confederate Soldier, which was incorrect; he was drafted into the Union Army for one year and served his full term. Simon's discharge from the army occurred in Nashville, Tennessee.

*Lick Creek Monument of the A.M.E. Meeting House Cemetery*
*Hoosier National Forest, Lick Creek Community (Since Destroyed)*

Ishmael Roberts' information, recorded on the monument, however, stated his internment at that location. But he was buried in Chatham County, North Carolina. The Roberts and Locust families were among the first African American settlers to come to Orange County, Indiana, before 1820. Jonathan Lindley, a Quaker, accompanied them. Johnathan came to Indiana in 1811, five years before the county's establishment and before Indiana became a State.

The Roberts family continued to move to Indiana and Ohio. "Eleven families traveled with a group of sympathetic Quakers in search of new land which forbade slavery. The settlers who were free citizens were fleeing racial persecution and increasingly restrictive laws against Free People of Color in North Carolina and other States.

Some of the other families traveled with different Quaker families who afforded them protection on their journey. By traveling with these Anglo neighbors, the Free People of Color also received the security of supportive farmers when they arrived in Orange County, Indiana."

According to the census records, ninety-six African Americans lived in Orange County, Indiana, in 1820. Moses Locust, Simon's father, was one of the first settlers of Orange County, Indiana. Moses Locust moved from North Carolina to Indiana sometime in the early 1820s.

Moses' name appeared on the 1830 U.S. Census and his wife, Ferebee, and sons Simon and John W. Locust. Moses began to purchase land in Indiana and made three additional land purchases. On August 20, 1832, he bought 40 acres; on June 14, 1836, he bought another 40 acres, and then on October 2, 1838, he purchased an additional 40 acres.

The first African Americans to purchase land in the Lick Creek area were Benjamin Roberts, Peter Lindley, Elias Roberts, and Moses Locust. Each man purchased his land by 1832. By 1855, the settlement reached its maximum size of 1,557 acres. By 1860, 260 African Americans lived in Orange County. Almost a third of them lived in Southeast Township in the Lick Creek Settlement, an integrated community.

Simon inherited land from his father, Moses, upon his death. Then he began to purchase land for himself and his family. Rev. Simon Locust purchased 173 acres of land on March 5, 1870, from John E. Hall and his wife, Margaret. Then he bought 200 acres of land on April 19, 1887, from James L. Lynd and his wife, Milly. Simon began to lose his land because his land was not producing enough crops, and he could not afford to pay his taxes. James L. Lynd purchased at public auction 200 acres of land, which was Simon Locust's property. It was auctioned off and purchased for nonpayment of debt.

Then Charles Edwards purchased at public auction 200 acres of Simon's land. The county auctioned off the property for nonpayment of a Common School Fund Mortgage, taken out on April 19 by Simon and Florence Locust. Simon lost more property due to his inability to pay taxes. Charles Edwards recorded a deed on March 22, 1897.

Many information sources referencing the Lick Creek Settlement residents were obtained from their freedom papers filed in the County Courthouse. They had to send to North Carolina to prove their "Free" status. Indiana had developed laws in the 1850s that no other Free People of Color could move into their State. So, the ones that were already there had to prove that they had a "Free" status before 1850.

Land Office Records, 1796-1907 for Moses Locust

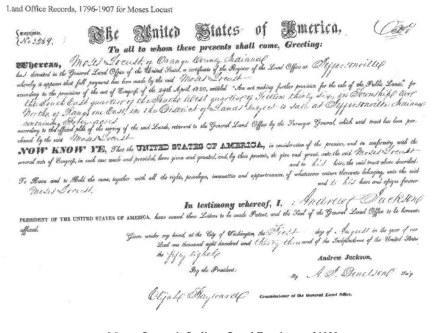

*Moses Locust's Indiana Land Purchase of 1833*

When the overseas slave trade ended, the practice of kidnapping free African Americans and selling them into slavery in Kentucky became prevalent. Once seized, these Melungeon's had little recourse. In a County Register of 1853, secured by an Indiana law, all Negroes and Mullatoes to submit a physical description. These descriptions often included distinguishing marks and required extensive statements provided by Anglo witnesses of their previous communities vouching for each of the registrants' free status and describing their good character.

A focal point of the Lick Creek Settlement was the church. In 1843, Thomas and Matilda Roberts sold one acre of their 120 acres to five trustees for its establishment. The deed stated that Elias Roberts, Mathew Thomas, Thomas Roberts, Isaac Scott, and Samuel Chandler erected a house or worship place. The members of the African Methodist Episcopal Church (A.M.E.) of the U.S.A. would use this building. The A.M.E. church operated from 1843 to 1869.

The A.M.E. church was near the site of the Colored Methodist Union Meeting House. The community built the Methodist Union Meeting House in 1837 on land owned by Ishmael Roberts. It is unclear when they abandoned the Methodist Union Meeting House, but the new A.M.E. Church probably replaced it. Near this church is the Thomas and Roberts family cemetery. There are at least 14 marked headstones. Burials occurred from 1856 to 1891.

The presence of professionally made headstones attests to the family's wealth. According to early histories, the last person to be buried there was Rev. Simon Locust in September 1891. Chambersburg, Indiana, was a station on the Underground Railroad. It was the first stop north of the Ohio River. When the Quakers escorted the African Americans there, they helped the families' resettlement process. It seems as though the former Eli Lindley's House may have been one of the homes on the Underground Railroad.

At the end of the Civil War, the population at Lick Creek began to decline sharply. By the early 1900s, the African Americans were gone. Many left the area in 1862. Since the war was in progress, the industry's boom was occurring in nearby cities, and racial pressure increased with the many anti-African American organizations. After these landowners left the area, their Anglo neighbors purchased the land.

These Anglo neighbors continued farming in the community until they were unable to pay their taxes. Many of them lost their land in the

1930s. This area is now part of the Hoosier National Forest and is the focus of ongoing archaeological research.

Nathan Locust lived in the Treme' community of New Orleans, where most of the Free People of Color lived. Many of them became tradesmen after the Civil War. Nathan and his wife were listed on 1873, 1874, 1878, and 1891 City Directories in Orleans Parish. He filed for his Civil War pension on May 15, 1888. Parish Deaths show that Nathan did not return to North Carolina and died in New Orleans on March 12, 1892.

Another family member, Charles Lucas, belonged to the family branch that did not move to North Carolina. He was born in Culpepper, Virginia, and was thirty-five years old when he enlisted in the Civil War. He was 5 feet, 8 inches tall, with a brown complexion, brown eyes, and black hair. He enrolled at Camp Casey, Virginia. Charles volunteered on the 14th day of November 1864. However, he did not survive the war. He died of smallpox in the Hospital at Harts Island, New York, in February 1865.

Some of Thomas's relatives were not able to receive their pensions. The military denied his cousin, Simon Locust's, pension claim. Simon's father, Moses Locust, was born in Robeson County, North Carolina, and moved to Lick Creek, Indiana. Avoiding the unfair practices against Free People of Color in that State. Simon was born in 1824 in Orange County, Indiana. He was 40 years old when the military-drafted him into the Civil War for one year's enlistment.

The type of pension that Thomas and Ellis received was called an Invalid Pension. Simon entered service on September 23, 1864, and was discharged on October 18, 1865, due to his service expiration. He first applied for a pension on September 24, 1885. He stated that he had contracted a disease of the feet.

Simon said that a disease of his feet and his legs caused swelling. He stated that this disease occurred while he was in service in the line of duty at Nashville, Tennessee. Concerning his military duty performed in December 1864, he said that he had rheumatism in an affidavit filed on August 16, 1886. Simon continued to submit affidavits requesting his pension. He appeared to become more frustrated as the years went by without success.

Simon had trouble finding the persons in the service with him and could verify his military time. One of his affidavits by the doctor said that he did not know whether Simon's name was Locus or Locust in a letter from Paoli, Indiana, dated October 2, 1888. In this letter, Simon asked about the state of his claim No. 550.390 for his original pension. He said that he had not heard from it for a long time. He assumed that they were still waiting for evidence.

Simon requested a man named Mr. G. Hazlewood write a letter to him:

For Original
No. 550390
Claimant Simon Locust,
Private
Co. "E" 13th Reg U.S.C. Inf.

Chambersburg, Orange Co. Indiana
February 24, 1891:

Court of Pensions

Dear Sir:

I write you requesting you to inform him why his pension is not granted by request of Simon Locust. He is old and unable to work and thinks he is neglected because he is an old Negro.

Yours,

G. Hazlewood.

Simon died shortly after this letter on September 24, 1891, at 67 years old. His wife continued the attempt to obtain a widow's pension. Florence Locust wrote to the U.S. Army many times about his retirement since he did not receive his award while still living.

By June 10, 1895, from Chambersburg, Orange County, Indiana, Florence wrote about her widow's pension. She addressed her inquiry to the President of the United States.

"Mr. President Sir, the President of the United States.

I cannot work for my support and almost destitute, and I feel compelled to ask you to please see the matter with my claim that I can't get it. It has been over one year since I heard from it. If you can do me very well, please do so as soon as you can.

Yours respectfully,

Florence Locus"

The Army justified not giving Simon or his widow, Florence, a pension after he died. They said he died of rheumatism, heart disease, and dropsy (swelling in the body now known as Edema). Simon did complain of swelling when he was seeking his pension.

There was a question about Florence's land ownership when the Army evaluated her request for a pension. The Army determined that she was not destitute because she had land and could sell it to obtain money.

Another determining factor for denying the widow's pension was that they did not have any dependent children. In one of her affidavits, Florence stated that she was with a child, yet, later documents did not mention the child again. Florence Locust also passed away without receiving her husband's invalid pension.

In the 1770's many of the Melungeon families left Virginia and relocated to North Carolina and later to Ohio and Indiana. When Thomas's ancestors left Virginia, they moved first to Northampton, North Carolina. Then they moved to the Counties of Robeson, Lenoir, Chowan, Chatham, Edgecombe, Nash, and some moved to Wake County. Many of these Free Men of Color fought in the American Revolution.

An incentive existed which allowed enslaved people to receive Freedom if they enlisted in the Revolutionary War. Thomas's ancestors were free before the Revolution and could trace their ancestry back to 1636. Many were already "Free" when they entered the Revolutionary war.

A great grandfather from Robeson County, North Carolina, Melungeon and Lumbee Indian, Ishmael Roberts, fought in the Revolutionary War. Ishmael received 640 Acres of land for his service. He was born in 1750, and his mother and grandmother were both free before him and produced Last Will and Testaments. Ishmael had fifteen children, and many of them left North Carolina in the early 1800s. They wanted to avoid the persecution that was now prevalent in North Carolina. Also, since many of them were tradesmen, they could not find work in North Carolina.

The Roberts family of North Carolina was free before the American Revolution. Ishmael Roberts, the patriarch, bought land in Orange County, Indiana, from the Federal Reserve in 1824. This purchase was probably in conjunction with his sons and grandsons' arrival, Wiley, Nelson, John, and Elias Roberts. They came with their family from North Carolina.

## Moses Locust in the 1830 United States Federal Census

| | |
|---|---|
| Name: | Locust [Moses Locust] |
| Home in 1830 (City, County, State): | Orange, Indiana |
| Free Colored Persons - Males - Under 10: | 2 |
| Free Colored Persons - Males - 36 thru 54: | 1 |
| Free Colored Persons - Females - 36 thru 54: | 1 |
| Total Free Colored Persons: | 4 |
| Total - All Persons (Free White, Slaves, Free Colored): | 4 |

Many free African American families sold their land in the early nineteenth century and headed west or remained in North Carolina as poor farm laborers. This migration was probably the consequence of a combination of deteriorating economic conditions and the restrictive "Free Negro Code" laws.

In 1826 and continuing through the 1850s, North Carolina passed a series of restrictive laws termed the Free Negro Code. In a book by John Hope Franklin, he stated that: "Free African Americans lost the right to vote and were required to obtain a license to carry a gun. Tensions arising from Nat Turner's slave rebellion in nearby Southampton County, Virginia, played a major role in the passage of these laws. In the 1830s, laws against the African American population helped divert poor whites' attention from their worsening economic conditions."

Many of Roberts' family members settled in Lick Creek, Indiana. Moses Locust and others developed their farming communities in the 1820s. Moses' children married into the families of other Free People of Color. He was another of Thomas's relatives who also purchased land and moved to Lick Creek. These Melungeon families traveled together and lived near each other.

"As early as 1814, Quakers in Washington County, Indiana, were aiding in the resettlement and education of former slaves. There were more than 250 African American residents of Orange County. Among them, nine families surnames were Roberts, six named Scott, two families of Duggers', Burnett's, and Thomas's and families named Chavers', Hawkins, Lynch, Locust, Sneed, Chandler, Newby, Weaver, Hathaway, Todd, Hamm, Smith, and Barton."

Some of these families moved into northern Hamilton County and established a community still known as Roberts Settlement. Other Roberts were among the earliest African American settlers in Vigo County, Indiana, in Lost Creek. The families shared the same ethnicities, Native American, African and European backgrounds as in the old South.

"They migrated for similar reasons and experienced broadly similar fates, both as farmers and African Americans attempting to create their autonomous communities." These Melungeon families grew in number because of migration from one community to the next, marriages among men and women from different neighborhoods, and residents are serving as ministers and teachers in other communities.

Besides, the Melungeon's shared interactions in common with each other were social, political, and military organizations, such as the African Methodist Episcopal (A.M.E.) Church, the Prince Hall Masons, the Republican Party, and the Civil War-era United States Colored Troops (USCT). Their experiences may not have been typical of all African Americans in the rural Midwest. Still, they intersected with a very substantial proportion of that Melungeon isolate.

Some of the Locust and Roberts family members who served in the American Revolution thought they would be safe. They continued to stay in Nash, Wilson, Wake, and Robeson Counties in North Carolina. They suffered despite their dedication to America and their service in the Revolutionary War against the British.

One of Thomas' cousins, Valentine Locust, who served in the Revolutionary War, actually experienced the tragedy of having his children kidnapped. An article in the Raleigh Register related facts of the kidnapping:

Raleigh Register

October 6, 1801

FREE NEGRO STEALERS.

ON the 29th Inftant, about Mid'
Night, four Men came to the Houfe of
VALENTINE LOCUST, an aged Free Negro,
Who refides on Leek Creek, in Wake
County, and calling at the Door to gain
Admittance, as foon as the Door was opened,
Two of them entered with Clubs, and inftan-
Taneoufly knocked down the old Man and his
Wife, and beat them to fuch a Degree as
fcarcely to leave Life; and whilft they were

in that Situation, the Robbers carried off
two of their Children, a Boy named Abſalom,
Aged about twelve Years, of a yellowiſh
Complexion, who is juſt able to read and
Write; a Girl, named Polly, age about five
Years, of a Complexion more yellow than
her Brother.
The Father of theſe Children is a reſpectable
and induſtrious old Man, who has hitherto
made ample Proviſions for himſelf and
family: and it is hoped, from the peculiar
Circumstances of his Caſe, ariſing from his
incapacity to bear Witneſs, except againſt
his own Colour, added to the diſtreſſed situation
he muſt be placed in after the Loſs of
his two Children, will awaken the Feelings
of the Humane, and that they will contribute
every Thing in their Power they may
tend to the detecting and puniſhing ſuch vile
Offenders.
It is ſuppoſed the Perpetrators of this Offence,
will endeavor to convey their Prey to
the State of Georgia, in the Character of
Slaves, for the Purpoſe of Traffic.

*Wake County, N. Carolina,*
*Sep. 30, 1801*

The Printers in the U. States who are
deſirous of detecting the Offenders will give
this a Place in their Papers.

Valentine's son, Absalom, and daughter, Polly, escaped the child
stealers' clutches. At the same time, they slept, and the children
returned to their parents. Several cases of child and adult kidnapping
were prevalent. Many were taken and then sold into slavery, which is
another reason that the families stayed near each other.

# Family Group Sheet for Caroline Carrie Locust

| Husband: | Peter Warters Fuller |
|---|---|
| Birth: | 1808 in Norfolk, Virginia |
| Marriage: | 25 Jan 1881 in Yazoo, MS |
| Death: | 09 Jun 1885 in Norfolk, VA; Died of old age |
| Burial: | Norfolk, Norfolk City, Virginia, USA |
| Father: | |
| Mother: | |

| Wife: | Caroline Carrie Locust |
|---|---|
| Birth: | 1806 in Robeson, Cumberland Co, NC |
| Death: | 26 Nov 1894 in Norfolk, VA; Living at 226 S. Halls St, Norfolk, VA |
| Burial: | Norfolk, Norfolk City, Virginia, USA |
| Father: | Isham Locus Lucas Sr. |
| Mother: | Margaret Maggie Roberts |
| Other Spouses: | James Medly (1835 in Wilson, North Carolina) |
| | Nn Jackson |

**Children:**

| 1 | Name: | Richard Locust |
|---|---|---|
| M | Birth: | 1833 in Kinston, Lenoir, North Carolina, USA |
| | Marriage: | 1869 in Nash, NC |
| | Spouse: | Esther Caraway |
| | Other Spouses: | Charlotte Hardy (19 Jan 1882 in Lenoir, North Carolina, USA) |

| 2 | Name: | Jane Gatsey Locust |
|---|---|---|
| F | Birth: | 1839 in Nash County, North Carolina; Listed as Mulatto on 1850 Kinston Census |
| | Marriage: | 1880 in Pitt, NC |
| | Spouse: | David Davis |
| | Other Spouses: | William Tayborn (21 Nov 1858 in Nash co., NC) |

| 3 | Name: | Eunice Fuller Bradshaw |
|---|---|---|
| F | Birth: | Feb 1844 in Grifton, Pitt, North Carolina, United States |
| | Death: | 1923 in Goldsboro, Wayne, North Carolina, United States |
| | Burial: | 1923 in Parkstown, Wayne, NC; Old Mill Cemetery |
| | Spouse: | Samuel Walter Jackson |
| | Other Spouses: | Nn Bradshaw |

| 4 | Name: | Thomas Locust Fuller |
|---|---|---|
| M | Birth: | 21 Apr 1847 in Grifton, Pitt, North Carolina |
| | Marriage: | May 1870 in Pitt, Lenoir, NC |
| | Death: | 03 Nov 1932 in Kinston, Lenoir Co, NC |
| | Spouse: | Manerva Nerva Dawson |
| | Other Spouses: | Beady Coward (15 Feb 1877 in Greene, North Carolina, USA) |

**Notes:**

Thomas Locust Fuller

# CHAPTER 7

## Mother Locust and Father Fuller

Thomas' father, Peter Fuller, appears first to be listed in the household of David Fuller, of Granville County, as the only enslaved person in 1810, then in 1820 as one of three enslaved persons (a male aged between the ages of 14 to 25 years old, then between the ages of 24 to 35 in the 1830 U.S. Census. By 1840, David Fuller does not have any enslaved persons in his household. DNA proves that Peter Fuller is Thomas Warters's son, a European enslaver who lived in Lenoir county.

He is an enslaved male listed on the 1850 and 1860 censuses in Charles Fuller's household. Thomas, Eunice, and their mother, Carrie, appeared on the 1850 and 1860 U.S. Censuses living next door to Charles Fuller. On that same census record is a Free Person Of Color child living on Charles' property, is most likely Carrie's son, Richard Locust. Since Peter was with the family on the 1870 census and the 1880 census, he must have lived near his children, Thomas and Eunice, in earlier years.

Charles Fuller and his wife, Nancy Dawson Fuller, lived next door to Caroline "Carrie" Locust. Benjamin Warters was living near them. Peter's occupation was listed as a blacksmith on the 1880 Wayne County U.S. Census. Caroline's surname is misspelled differently on various Census records.

Since Caroline was listed as the head of the household in 1850 with three children, Thomas, Eunice, and Cathy, Peter must not have lived in the home with them but nearby. He appears to live in the Charles Fuller and Nancy Dawson Fuller household or a Warters' family household as an enslaved blacksmith. Free People of Color (with a trade) may bind themselves to a person to earn money for their families. Additionally, there is not an occupation stated for Caroline.

Caroline "Carrie" Locust was the mother of four children. Her first son, Richard Locust, was born in 1833 in Kinston, Lenoir County, NC. Richard's father was Jim Medley, and his first wife and the mother

111

of Richard Locust Junior was Esther Carroway. Richard's third wife was Charlotte Hardy. He had one son with Susan Tilghman and had two sons and two daughters with Esther Easter Grainge. He then married Charlotte Hardy, and they had one daughter together.

Caroline's second child, Catherine Jane Gatsy Locust, born in 1838, married David Davis. His first wife was Nancy Tyler, who lived next door to Thomas' mother, Caroline, and was listed as "Mulatto." Most Free People of Color are classified Mulatto as Caroline and Nancy were, like many others living in North Carolina during this period. The Locust family and the Tyler's had Native American ancestry yet were still listed as Mulatto.

The term "Mulatto" was a catchall phrase used for people who were of diverse ancestry. These individuals could have been Anglo-African, Indian-African, Indian-Anglo, or any other combination of different ethnicities. Anyone considered "Non-White" during this time could have their lands taken away from them and lose many of their privileges. If Native Americans lived outside of the reservation, it was common not to list them as Native Americans on the Census.

The following interview held by the North Carolina Senate explains the consensus of the term "Mulatto" related to the Lucas/Locus(t), Jones, Archer, Artis, Newsome, and Roberts families of Robeson County. These names were a few of those listed as Free Person of Color surnames.

"1871…The North Carolina Joint Senate and House Committee interviewed Robeson County Judge Giles Leitch about the **"Free Persons of Color"** residing within his county:

Senate: Half of the colored population?

Leitch: Yes, sir; half of the colored population of Robeson County were never slaves at all

Senate: What are they; *are they Negroes?*

Leitch: Well, sir, I desire to tell you the truth as near as I can, but I do not know what they are; I think *they are a mixture of Spanish, Portuguese and Indian.*

Senate: You think they are mixed Negroes and Indians.

Leitch: *I do not think* that in that class of population *there is much Negro blood at all* of that half of the *colored population* that I have attempted to describe all have always been free... *They are called 'Mulattoes'* that is the name they are known by, as *contradistinguished from Negroes...I think they are of Indian origin.*

Senate: I understand you to say that these seven or eight hundred persons that *you designate as mulattoes are not Negroes* but are *a mixture of Portuguese and Spanish, white blood, and Indian blood,* you think they are not generally Negroes?

Leitch: I do not think the Negro blood predominates.

Senate: the word 'mulatto' means a cross between the white and the Negro?

Leitch: Yes, sir.

Senate: You do not mean the word to be understood in that sense when applied to these people?

Leitch: I really do not know how to describe those people."

(Even a person not considered to bear Negro ancestry might be called Mulattoes as late as the 1870s the term 'Portuguese' used here to infer Spanish and Indian ancestry' Portuguese' was also used by persons of North Carolina origin residing in South Carolina, Tennessee, etc. to describe mixed Indian-white persons from the North Carolina/Virginia border area during this time."

The Tylers were Catawba Indians, and Nancy Tyler lived next door to Caroline. Nancy might have been the daughter of Indian Nan, and since she was living next door to Caroline and her children, they might be relatives.

Caroline's daughter Jane's last name was Jackson. Caroline may have been married to a man named "Jackson" before she married Peter Warters Fuller. Peter Warters and Caroline Jackson married in Mississippi in 1881. This record might have been the legitimization of their marriage. Peter used the "Warters" surname when he lived with Caroline on the 1870 Census. It is believed that Peter was enslaved by Thomas Warters, and he took that surname when he was emancipated.

Thomas' grandfather, Isham Locust, told him about a court case published in the Louisa County Historical Society's Journal about their relatives. "Indian Joe versus Hutchinson Capias, Apl 1768, Condl. Order 12 Apl. Yesterday the order was discharged as not guilty and issued.

This court case accused Plaintiff, Indian Joe, the brother of Indian Nan, of being a Slave, and he replied that he was a Freeman. Court case suits of Indian Joe, Indian Nan, Indian Betty, and Indian Bartlett presented in the Louisa County Courts. Samuel Clark was a witness on behalf of Indian Nan, Indian Bartlett, Indian Priss, and Indian Betty. Samuel is "their next best friend." In this case, Plaintiffs about Indian Joe, son of Priss Tyree, (or Tyler), a Catawba girl.

The testimony of Samuel Clark, a witness for the said plaintiff, "was that he was acquainted with Priss. She was a reputed Catawba, and she told him that as a Catawba, her head had been tied to a board to make it flat. He said that he was acquainted with the Catawba Nation. It was their custom to press their infants' heads flat and that he is, thereby, convinced she was a Catawba.

Clark heard from Hicks' daughter that Priss was not a slave, and he bought her away from the Catawba Nation, and her father sold her for a horse of small value. He also said that Paul Hess was an Indian trader who told him that he was with Hicks when he bought Priss from the Nation, and Hicks and Paul Hess are now dead.

When Hicks' daughter was about 16, she understood that Priss was about 15 or 16 years of age and well grown. She also said that before Mr. Williams paid the said purchase money, the said girl was not a slave. But she had been induced by Hicks to leave the Catawba Nation and come to Virginia. She told him that the girl said a board being tied to her head to make it flat (as was the custom of the Catawba tribe).

Williams refused to pay until he received Davis's bond to indemnify him if it should be found that the girl was not a slave. Williams wanted to move towards the Catawba Nation.

In July 1768, age 35, Indian Joe, said to be the son of Priss. This Indian woman belonged to John Thompson, who was deceased, and that the said woman died while John Thompson possessed her. Indian Joe, who could be eligible for his freedom as a poor person. Joe complains that he is in Charles Hutchison's custody, that he is not a slave and has the right to liberty by the "law of the land."

That he believed that the said petitioner to be the son of the said Priss as she suckled him, the defendant, by his attorney, objected as being insufficient. The case allowed to go to the jury, formed a verdict for the petitioner by consent of parties."

Indian Nan vs. Thompson Exors:

"Samuel Clark, age 54 years, and sayeth that he is of Prince George County, now Dinwiddie County, about 34 years old, and the daughter of Capt. Hicks. The Indian trader, named Tabitha Crawley, asked this deponent what happened to the Indian girl named Priss? He told her she was sold to John Thompson, merchant of Hanover County.

That the said Tabitha Crowley said, it was very hard for Davis who told this despond. Who persuaded the girl to go with him. She was an alone girl, her mother being dead. That she should be a slave because her father and Captain Hicks had persuaded her from the Indian nation.

Portilo, the Indian trader, was standing by and said she ought not to be a slave, that she was at the Catawba Nation when Capt. Hicks bought her away, and Hicks sold the Indian girl Priss to John Davis. Then Davis sold her to Thomas Williams, and Williams sold her to John Thompson, a merchant of Hanover County, February 9, 1771." The Indian Tylers won their freedom in 1771.

From the mid-1700s to the early 1800s, Free People of Color were under attack. After the Nat Turner Rebellion, though it occurred in Virginia, the case made their North Carolina neighbors suspicious of the Free People of Color. Anglos began to resent the Melungeon's "Free" status, and life became uncomfortable for them in North Carolina.

Thomas's family was no exception; his grandfather, Isham Locust, and his great uncle and aunt were indentured for many years. These indentures of children were little more than slavery. If they attempted to run away, rewards are placed on their heads to bring them back to the people who bound them.

Some of Thomas's ancestors originally lived in Virginia. More of them inhabited that State; they married into the Native American population. Many of the men married English women. Some Englishmen married African women, and these relationships started building the community called the "Tri-Racial Isolates."

More stringent laws that forbade people from freeing their slaves were enacted. Around the 1750s, the laws against the Free People of Color became more restrictive. Free People of Color were forced to leave Virginia with their Anglo wives and escaped to North Carolina. Melungeons were later subject to increasingly stringent laws.

The Melungeons were free to marry whom they wanted. Still, they could not stay in Virginia because of State passed laws that instructed them to leave its territory. Since Thomas's family knew that they were breaking the law and feared reprisals, they left Virginia as not to be enslaved.

These Free Persons of Color might have been chiefly Native American or European-American. Still, there were Anglos like Walter Ashby Plecker, who hated the Melungeon people. He was so vicious against them that he did not want them to attend schools with Anglo students. He went out of his way in an attempt to discover if a person had any African ancestry in their family so that he could deny them their rights to an education.

Plecker did not want them to claim their Native American heritage. If Plecker could prove or speculate that any persons were descendants of Africans, he fought diligently to have them classified as purely African. He took away their right to their Native American heritage. He believed that if a Native American married an Anglo, they were considered as Native American. Still, if they married a person of African descent, he stated that they had no rights to their Native ancestry. He spent most of his life harassing Melungeons and rejecting their applications for equal education.

Tori Talbot's article in the Encyclopedia of Virginia discusses, "Walter Ashby Plecker was a physician and the first Virginia state registrar of vital statistics, a position he served in from 1912 until1946. He was a staunch promoter of eugenics, a discredited movement aimed at scientifically proving white racial superiority and justifying non-white people's marginalization.

Employing Virginia's Act to Preserve Racial Integrity (1924), Plecker effectively separated Virginia citizens into two simplified racial categories: white and colored. The law remained in effect until 1967 when the United States Supreme Court overturned it in Loving v. Virginia. The court case required a racial description of every person to be recorded at birth while criminalizing marriages between whites and non-whites.

Plecker's policies used deceptive scientific evidence to deem African Americans as a lesser class of human beings. He targeted poor Whites and anyone he, or other eugenicists, considered "feebleminded." Asserting that Virginia Indians were, in fact, "mixed-blooded negroes," Plecker also pressured state agencies into reclassifying Indians as "colored." The policy's legacy was effectively to erase "Indian" as an identity and has made it difficult for Virginia Indians to gain state and federal recognition.'

Walter Plecker admired Hitler and accepted many of his views, including the idea of a "pure race." The irony is that many of the people he considered "White" had African and Native American ancestry. Since many of the Melungeons did not look as though they could be of African or Native American descent, it was difficult to classify them by ethnicities.

Many Free People of Color left the States of Virginia and North Carolina. They moved to Tennessee and other states where people did not know their ethnic makeup. Some of them began to "Pass" and moved into mainstream Anglo society.

Many Melungeon families began to move to Canada in the 1830s. Some moved to Liberia, including members of the Roberts family. One such member, Joseph Jenkins Roberts, was born March 15, 1809, in Norfolk County, Virginia. His parents were James Roberts, born in 1777, and Amelia Milly Jenkins, born in 1789. Joseph moved to Liberia in 1829 and became the first African American Governor there from 1841 to 1847. He then served as the first President of Liberia after they received their Independence. He held that office from 1847 to 1856 and then again from 1872 to 1876.

Between his Presidencies, Joseph Roberts served in the Liberian Army and held a Major General's military rank. He was also a diplomatic representative for France and Great Britain. He died in Monrovia, Montserrado, Liberia, while still in office on February 24, 1876. Liberia's main airport, Roberts International Airport, is named for Joseph and his likeness is on the Liberian $10.00 bill.

# CHAPTER 8

## Beginnings of the Melungeon Locust's

Thomas's mother told him stories of his family's origins. He learned that his fifth great-grandmother was born two hundred and two years before him in England. His fifth great grandfather was born two hundred and twenty-nine years before him in Angola, Africa. Thomas knew about his distant great grandmother, Elizabeth Lucas, and his distant great grandfather, John Kecotan, mainly referred to as just "Jack" or "Jack the Negro."

Elizabeth Lucie Lucas and Jack Kecotan were the Locust Melungeon family's progenitors, and Thomas' ancestry traced to this union. Thomas' 5th great-grandmother, Elizabeth, was born in England in 1646. Elizabeth was an indentured servant in Charles City County, Virginia.

She was an English Servant maid indentured to Rice Hoe Senior. Elizabeth had a relationship with an African man, John Kecotan. When Elizabeth died in 1665, she was nineteen years old. Her son was bound out (indentured) to Howell Pryse, like most free children of color. It was in this year that Jack appealed to the Governor and Council of Virginia for his freedom.

"John the Negro," now a servant of Rice Hooe Jr., was in a court battle over whether he should be released from servitude. The documents left by Rice Hooe Sr. dictated that he agreed to remove Jack from his bondage, and Rice Hooe Jr. refused to give him his freedom. He was finally freed from Indenture on 8 Feb 1666.

Jack served an indenture to Rice Hoe Sr, and on 26 November 1653, Hoe, since deceased, had stated that John should be free after serving eleven more years. Hoe added, "provided that he, the sd Negro doth carefully and honestly performe his labour." Hoe's son, Rice Hoe, Jr., refused to release him, claiming that he had not lived up to the agreement. But the court sided with Jack, and they removed him from his bondage in 1666.

Paul Heinegg, the noted Free Person of Color expert and genealogist, says about this family:

"The Lucas-Locust family most likely originated in Charles City County, Virginia. There the churchwardens of Weynoke Parish presented Elizabeth Lucie for having a base-born child by an unknown father. Her son, a "molotto boy the sonne of Elizabeth Lucie dec'd," was bound to Howell Pryse on 4 December 1665."

Jack (John[1] Tann) "was a negro servant to Mr. Rice Hoe," who was ordered freed from his service on 8 February 1665/6 by a note given him by his former master, Rice Hoe, Sr."

Information passed down through the family to Thomas concerning these great grandparents was taken from another servant's statement. Margaret Barker was a former servant of Rice Hoe, and she claimed, "Hoe never had a servant maid, but the sd Jack the Negro lay w'th her or got her w'th child" [Orders 1655-65, 601, 617, 618, 632].

One of Hoe's descendants, Howson Hoe of Prince William County, was the master of Hester Lucas, a "mulatto woman servant" whose son was bound to Hoe in 1763."The Locust family were servants of the Hoe family for many years.

Thomas's great grandparent's neighbor, Margaret Barker, was a European mid-wife and testified that she delivered several children. She provided derogatory testimony in Jack Kecotan's case. At the time of her testimony before the courts, she was a woman (47 years old) when she testified against the 47-year-old John Kecotan in 1665. This particular lady, named Margaret Barker, was not related to Jack Tann and Elizabeth Lucie Lucas's parentage.

Margaret Barker was born in Scituate, Plymouth, Massachusetts, and lived there until she was thirty-two years old before relocating to Virginia. From her statement, it appears that John Kecatan had more than one child. He had a daughter with Charles Magnars, a dark-complexioned child, and a son he had with Elizabeth Lucas, born in 1665. Another son, John Kecotan II, was born in 1670.

His son, John Kiketan/ Kicotan II, was born about 1670 and was a seven-year-old "Mollato boy" bound until 24 years of age on 3 November 1677. Then Stephen Lewis sold the remainder of his indenture to William Edwards by Surry County deed for 2,500 pounds of tobacco [DW 2:157]. John was called a "Molatto boy, Jno. Kikeson(?)" He was named in a 7 May 1678 Surry County court suit between William Edwards and Stephen Luies [Haun, *Surry County Court Records*, III:381]."

There was court testimony which occurred in Charles City County, Virginia, concerning Jack Kecatan: "The deposicon of Margret Barker, aged 47 or thereabouts exai'ed and sworne this 28th day of October 1665: "That your depon't being about 15 yeares since Scituate and living by Mr. Rice Hoe senr, upon his land and being a comon reteiner to the howse, this depon't did bring one Charles Magnars's wife, to a bed of a Girle......and the sd Magnas lay it to Mr. Hoes' Negro Jack. He did acknowledge it to be his.

And this depon't did about that time see the said Negro Jack one night take an English wench of Mr. Hoes by the arms, and had her out of Mr. Hoes milk house into the orchyard and then throw her upon a bench and gott upon her and this depon't run and got an axe and flung at the said negro and cut him on the leg.

Moreover, the neighbors sayd it had been his standard practice. These things together with the complaint of John Banister and Edward Spatiatt and diverse others of the neighbors to Mr. Hoe concerning his Negro Jack's killing of their hogs.

They threatened to kill the said Negro, whereupon Mr. Hoe for prevencon of future mischiefe to his neighbors and to secure his Negro's Life did to your depon'ts knowledge give the said Negro a note which was writt by Capt Roger Marshall vihich the said Hoe sayd was not dated which did expresse he should serve some certeine time and then made him beleeve, upon his good behaviour he should be free.

But it was not made, as Mr. Hoe Senr sayd, with any reall intent to set him free, but onely to make him behave himselfe better that the neighbors might have no such cause of complaint nor him in such feare of loseing his Negro being then threatened by severall people to be kill'd."

But to this dept's knowledge after this note made to the sd' Negro for some short time he did behave himselfe something better than he did before, but afterward he did fly out againe. And for five or six yeares after that this depon't lived there, the sd Hoe had never a serv't maid but the sd Jack the negro lay w'th her or got her w'th child, w'ch this depon't was very knowing of, and del'red one of them of a Negro child, she being an English woman. She being asked who was the father of it sayd, The abovesd Jack the Negro, and he asked, acknowledged it to be his."

Jack may have received his surname, Kecatan, when it was the original name for Elizabeth City, Virginia. During the muster of 1625, 23 Africans and a single Indian lived in the Jamestown community. All servants resided on plantations and scattered from the mouth of the James to Flowerdew Hundred. During this period, the river was the highway for goods' transportation. Many one-hundred-acre plantations dotted along the James River.

Many of the plantations along the James became the original shires or cities of Colonial Virginia. Africans probably lived in houses separate from their European masters. The 1625 muster included a list of the Europeans that arrived and the ships' names on which they traveled to the new world. There was very little information given about the early African arrivals.

Three African males and five females lived in one Jamestown household. There were four African men, two women, and a child living in the Virginia Colony. An African man named John Pedro lived in the home of Francis West of Elizabeth City.

Another African called Edward from the 1624 Muster still lived with Richard Kingsmill. Capt. Pierce's African female, Angelo, said to have come to Virginia on the Treasure in 1619, was living there. By 1625, Capt. Tucker's indentured servants, Anthony and Isabella, lived in Elizabeth City with their son, William.

Elizabeth Lucas came into Colonial Virginia when the Colonists used indentured servants from Europe to clear their lands and take care of their residences. Elizabeth had brothers who also came to America during this time. Africans were also indentured servants during this period.

"These indentured servants worked together, socialized together, and even ran away together." Since these associations had little to do with color and more to do with caste or class, it determined whom a person married or with whom fathered or mothered their children. This period was a precursor to the time of chattel slavery. Indentured servants who came to Jamestown from Africa could work their assigned time. Then they could receive land after completing their indenture.

Elizabeth Lucas and other European women came to the Colonies as indentured servants. They were of the same caste or class as other indentured servants. Whether European, Native American or African, servant partners received the same classification status as those they worked alongside. The church opposed individuals having children out of wedlock. Men were shamed in the church courtyard or placed in stocks, and women were given lashes for having illegitimate children.

There were very few women in the Colonies at the time. They were not free to marry the English men considered to be their masters. Female servants also were not allowed to marry until they had completed their indentures. These conditions prompted many indentured servants to have relationships with people of different nationalities since they worked alongside them.

Indentured servants shared camaraderie while being equally mistreated by their owners. These owners felt as though they could treat their servants in any manner they saw fit. The so-called "Masters" could beat their servants to death with no repercussions. They could starve them, and a greedy owner typically made his servants work twelve hours a day and seven days a week.

Many of these servants experienced hard labor. Documents survive that proved that European indentured servants contacted their families in England and told them of their mistreatment at their masters' hands. Thomas Best, the European seventh great grandfather of Rosetta's husband, Robie Best, was one of the British indentured servants in 1622. He said "that his master (as he called him) Mr. Atkins, sold him like a slave for 150 pounds sterling almost as soon as he got there."

Thomas Best was shocked by the blatant mistreatment of servants and believed that Europeans should not be sold and then resold. He also stated that Mr. Atkins was dishonest because he was lead to believe that he would have a fair indenture and live comfortably in the new world. Thomas Best wrote to his brother in England on April 12, 1623, that he was starving to the point of exhaustion. His name appeared on the February 1624 Muster, which demonstrates that he survived the 'Powhatan Uprising' and lived in Elizabeth City, Virginia.

"Like a Slave," said Thomas Best. To buy and sell servants for years was not the same as buying and "selling" men and women for life and their unborn children with them. The servitude of Thomas Best and his contemporaries was not a function of their race or nationality. "Nevertheless, in the treatment of labor in boom-time Virginia and the rising hatred of Indians, we can begin to discern some of the forces that would later link slavery to freedom."

Some Englishmen were against indentures and stated that "this buying and selling men and boies" was unacceptable. This behavior was considered scandalous by 1619. John Rolfe noted, "these indentures held in England a thing most intolerable."

Captain John Smith also denounced the practices of indenture. He said the "pride, covetousness, extortion, and oppress of men who sold even men, women and children for who will give the most." It would be better, he said, "that these profiteers be made such merchandise themselves than suffered any longer to use that trade."

Another of Mr. Atkin's indentured servants wrote to his brother in England and said he was only given about a quart of corn a day to eat. He said he had just a tiny amount of water to drink. He stated that he was starving "in such a severe way" that he elicited his brother's assistance.

Henry Brigg's brother was a merchant still living in England. His servant brother asked him to send him goods to sell so that he could try to make a living, in addition to his indentured servitude. This British servant said that he worked 12 hours a day felling trees, which was not easy work.

This type of injustice forced many indentured servants to run away together. In 1625 Thomas Weston refused to carry servants in his ship from Canada to Virginia. He said that "servants were sold here upp and downe like horses, and there he held it not lawful to carie any."

Indentured servants could not marry because their masters did not want to lose their property. It did not matter what the ethnicity of the indentured servant was to determine their likelihood of abuse. Suppose that "particular" master thought he did not have enough money or was losing money. In that case, he could sell his indenture to another person. Another Englishman stated that his master sold his indentureship four times before he arrived in the Virginia Colony.

One hundred women arrived in Jamestown in 1619 from Europe, recruited to come to the Colonies to marry the Planters who were already there. When Europe began recruiting indentured servants, they concentrated on men because clearing lands is heavy work.

Planters were beginning to feel loneliness and homesickness. The Proprietors in England wanted the Planters to remain in the Colonies and produce more tobacco for British sale and use. Therefore, women were a way of appeasing these Planters and encouraging them to stay in the new world.

During the Powhatan insurrection in 1622, there were some women in the Jamestowne Colony. About twenty of these women were from Martin's Hundred, and they were the only captives taken by the Powhatan Indians. The male colonists did not attempt to rescue the women and left them for a while with the Native Americans. Some community men finally decided to save the women and negotiate with the Native Americans on their release.

"The husband of Jane Dickenson, one of these women, had been killed in the insurrection. Mr. Pott, who held her deceased husband's indenture, required her to complete her husband's obligation, which had three years left on it. Jane not only had to serve her husband's full three-year indenture. But, to add insult to injury, she had to give Pott extra time to pay him back for the glass beads that he gave to the Native Americans for her release. She petitioned in March 1624 for her freedom from Mr. Pott's slavery."

Thomas's ancestor, Elizabeth Lucas, was also admonished for having a son out of wedlock. She was like many other women of her day. Physical whippings or admonishments by the Burgesses and people of the church did not deter the behavior. The punishments did not keep individuals from either marrying each other or having children again. There is evidence of women having additional children even after whipping. These were the conditions under which Thomas's great grandmother, Elizabeth Lucas, was living.

Colonial America was troubled with a disease. When the new servants disembarked the ships, they had dysentery and other diseases. Diseases were prevalent due to the passengers' malnourishment on the vessels during England's passage to the Colonies. The "Starving Time" created an atmosphere fraught with distress because many colonists died. Servants were lying in the streets dead because of slow burial practices.

British persons coming into colonies, at that time, were primarily indentured servants. In England, they requested more people who would work the tobacco farms in the Virginia Colony. The consequences of the constant demand for labor eventually made it harder to maintain people who could handle the rapidly growing tobacco crops. England was starving for tobacco because of the very high demand.

This greed for tobacco prompted the need for slave labor. Slavery occurred because it became more desirable to the colonists to hold men and women for life. The Europeans were completing their indentures and moving on. So the Virginia Company needed another labor source to replace the English indentured servants. Earlier indentured servants were obtaining land of their own, so Planters' sources of labor decreased dramatically. To increase work, they began the system of chattel slavery.

However, many people in England did not agree with these practices. They thought that the European indentures were not a good practice. The British realized that the servants who came from England had been beaten and otherwise mistreated.

Many of these servants said that they cried themselves to sleep at night because they had nowhere to turn. Many of those same men even committed suicide. There were deaths all around them because of mistreatment, starvation, and disease. Yet, the Masters wanted them to continue working themselves, many times to death! It was a sad time for many of those poor servants.

During this period, there were many unscrupulous practices to obtain additional labor in the American Colonies. Europeans, including ship captains (or their crew), would get men drunk, kidnap them, and put them on ships. They would also attack them by hitting them in the head and placing them on board a vessel unconscious to be deemed, new servants.

Another devious practice to obtain labor was by accusing people of theft and other petty crimes in England so men would become criminals. These men could take the jail option in England or free in America as servants; they chose the latter. Many men with the prospect of being prisoners thought it better to go to the American colonies rather than staying in England and subjected to cruelty in British prisons.

However, the English servants' expectations of the New World fell short of the actual conditions. Africans sold into the British Colonies did not expect fairness. Nor did they receive it. It was traditional that Africans warred against other tribes as others had done for centuries. They would capture opposing tribe members and would then enslave their captives. The difference between these African warring tribes and British enslavement was that the enslaved Africans could earn their freedom and marry into the enslaved tribes' families within a certain number of years.

The American chattel slavery system was quite different because greed permeated that particular endeavor. When the British discovered the decline of English indentures, they needed to devise another plan. Europeans could write home and let their parents, friends, and family know what was transpiring in the Colonies. It was easier for Europeans to relate to loved ones about their mistreatment.

The Colonists' next choice for slaves was the Native Americans, and enslaving them was unsuccessful. Though some warring tribes of Native Americans sold their captures into slavery to the Colonists, there were contemporary issues to consider. Native Americans' enslavement was not successful because they did not make good servants and ran away since they knew the land.

African enslavement was more permanent and profitable. Portuguese men have participated in the slave trade since the 1400s. When the need for tobacco increased, it made more sense to bring servants from another country and take away their ability to communicate with each other. When captors sold Africans into foreign lands, there was nowhere for them to run, even though some tried. "A servant in Virginia, as long as his term had not expired, was a machine to make tobacco for somebody else."

From a York County, Virginia court record dated July 9, 1640, Hugh Gwyn had three indentured servants run away from him and were later captured in Maryland. One man was Victor, a Dutchman; another was James Gregory, a Scotchman, and the other one was John Punch, an African.

The court meted out the punishment by issuing thirty stripes apiece. Each European served the balance of their three-year indenture. Then they were given one additional year when their contracts expired. But, the African servant unfairly received an unspeakable penalty:

"The third being a Negro named John Punch shall serve his said master and his assigns for a time of his natural Life here or elsewhere." It was one of the first evidence of an African's enslavement for life in Colonial America.

During the 1640s, there were still other Africans who were already free, and many had children. They were the descendants of the original Africans who came to Jamestowne in 1619 and 1628. Since the mother's status determined any Person of Color's condition, the children would be free if the mother were free. As long as a person could prove that their family had always been free, they would continue their "legal right" to freedom.

This law clarified the slavery system and the rights of people of color. The decision of whether a person of color could be free did not rest on parentage alone. Less frequently, European men fathered children. Though they were considered free, the laws changed to accommodate slavery. If every child fathered by a European man were "Free," then the enslaved number would be reduced dramatically. Slavery was, of course, a profitable business that supported the tobacco trade and later the cotton and sugar trade.

Free African Americans were also in danger of having their children stolen and sold into slavery. Drury Tann, Thomas's cousin, in his Revolutionary War pension application on 7 March 1834, declared in Southampton County, Virginia court that:

*"he was stolen from his parents when a small boy by persons unknown to him, who were carrying him to sell him into slavery, and had gotten with him and other stolen property as far as the Mountains on their way, that his parents made complaint to a Mr. Tanner Alford who was Then a magistrate in the county of Wake State of North Carolina to get me back from Those who had stolen me and he did pursue the Rogues & overtook Them at the mountains and took me from Them."*

129

| Table 3. Number of Persons in the Households of Families who had Been Free During the Colonial Period - 1810 Census | | |
|---|---|---|
| Family Name | Virginia | North Carolina |
| Anderson | 7 | 52 |
| Archer | 9 | 51 |
| Artis(t) | 86 | 38 |
| Banks | 54 | 28 |
| Bass | 21 | 80 |
| Battles | 25 | |
| Be(a)vans | 26 | |
| Beverly | 79 | |
| Bunda(y) | 70 | |
| Charity | 41 | |
| Chavis/ Chavers | 46 | 159 |
| Cousins | 52 | 6 |
| Cuffee | 96 | |
| Cumbo | | 43 |
| Day | 46 | 13 |
| Elliott | 43 | |
| Fuller | 28 | 3 |
| Going/ Gowen | 105 | 62 |
| Haithcock | 9 | 70 |
| Hammons | | 95 |
| Harman | | 37 |
| Howell | 37 | |
| James | | 69 |
| Johns | 36 | |
| Ligan/ Ligon | 39 | |
| Locklear | | 76 |
| Locus/ Lucas | 100 | 25 |
| Meekins | 26 | |
| Moore | | 65 |
| Nickens | 64 | 6 |
| Overton | | 58 |
| Oxendine | | 32 |
| Pin(n) | | 48 |

| | | |
|---|---|---|
| Reed | 12 | 43 |
| Revell | | 35 |
| Rich | 64 | |
| Richardson | | 58 |
| Roberts | | 111 |
| Sample | 36 | |
| Sparrow | 19 | |
| Valentine | 55 | 7 |
| Vena/ Venie | 64 | |
| Walden | 24 | 87 |
| Weaver | 64 | 37 |

An unfair practice perpetrated against Free Men of Color was Anglos. They claimed these men were vagrants and forced them into Revolutionary War service. Also, some enslaved men went into the service in the place of their enslavers after promises of freedom. Since slavery was still alive and well in Virginia and North Carolina, some enslavers reneged on their promise and re-enslaved the African Americans who fought in their place.

The Locust family defied many challenges. But, their designation of "Free People of Color" did not exempt them from the tribulations. Being indentured from infancy, forced into military service, paying discriminatory taxes, numerous lawsuits, physical attacks, burglary, and kidnapping were just a few of their injustices.

# Family Group Sheet for Jane Locus

| Husband: | Unknown Partner |
|---|---|
| Father: | |
| Mother: | |

| Wife: | Jane Locus |
|---|---|
| Birth: | 1757 in VA |
| Death: | 1792 in Nash Co, NC |
| Father: | Francis Locust |
| Mother: | Hannah Jeffries |

## Children:

| 1 M | | |
|---|---|---|
| | Name: | Isham Locus Lucas Sr. |
| | Birth: | 1776 in Nash Co, NC; FPOC bound to Lazarus Pope, then "bound unto Drury Taylor until he attains the age of 21 years, now 12 years old to Learn the art of Mystery Planter" |
| | Death: | 1869 in Cumberland Co., NC |
| | Marriage: | 26 Aug 1820 in Robeson, NC; Elthered Newsome was bondsman |
| | Spouse: | Margaret Maggie Roberts |

| 2 F | | |
|---|---|---|
| | Name: | Martha "Sally" Lucas |
| | Birth: | 1778 in Nash County, NC. USA; Free Person of Color "bound unto Drury Taylor untill She arrive to the age of Eighteen aged at this time fourteen Years to Learn the art and Mystery of Carding and Spinniing" |
| | Death: | 1854 in Nash County, North Carolina |
| | Marriage: | 01 Jan 1823 in Nash, NC |
| | Spouse: | Nn Lewton |

| 3 M | | |
|---|---|---|
| | Name: | Burwell Locust Pope |
| | Birth: | 1779 in Nash County, NC, USA; Apprenticed first to Lazarus Pope and then to Drury Taylor |
| | Death: | Bef. 1880 in NC |
| | Marriage: | 03 Jun 1811 in Wake, North Carolina, USA; Bondsman Dempsy Pope |
| | Spouse: | Betsey Gowen |
| | Other Spouses: | Lively Davis (24 Dec 1833 in Wake, North Carolina, USA) Bethena Scott (11 May 1842 in Wake Co NC) Phoebe Anderson |

## Notes:

### Isham Locus Lucas Sr.

Isham Lucas is listed as a free person of color on the 1810 US Census in Lenoir County, NC. His name is spelled wrong (Jham Lucas) with 3 persons in his household.

# CHAPTER 9

## The Catawba and Cherokee

Thomas Locust's grandfather, Isham Locust, was Native American, a Catawba Cherokee. His mother was Jane Locus, and he was born out of wedlock. Isham's birth caused him to be indentured early in life. Isham changed indentures to several different men. Yet, they continued his assigned period of twenty-one years of the contract. Court documents support him and his siblings' indentures.

An excerpt from Nash County, North Carolina's Court entry 278-July Court 1779, states: "Nash County Court ordered that Isham Locas, Martha Locas, and Burwell Locas, three base begotten children, be bound unto Lazarus Pope. The children aged as follows: Isham 3 years old, Martha 4 years old, and Burwell 2 months old, to learn the art and mystery of planters for the boys and the girl, carding & spinning."

This court excerpt demonstrates Isham's birth was in 1776, Martha was born in 1775, and their baby brother, Burwell, was born May 1779. Burwell, an infant, was also taken away from his mother, Jane, and indentured for twenty-one years. Free Children of Color, taken from their single or widowed mothers, were bound to another person for extended periods.

Isham, Martha, and Burwell's first indenture was with a Planter, Lazarus Pope, born around 1760. Lazarus and his wife, Barbara Jackson, were responsible for Isham and his brother, Burwell, and Martha's sister. Lazarus Pope died a few months after November 1779, and the children were later bound to Drury Taylor, his brother-in-law. Drury's wife was Rosamond Jincy Jackson, Barbara Jackson Pope's sister.

Just three years later, after the 1779 indenture, all three children were re-indentured to another family in January 1782: "Item 611 - Ordered that Martha, Isham & Burwell Locust, children of Jane Locus, be Bound to Peter Hatten. Sally (Martha) to live until she attains to the age of Eighteen, the two Boys until they Attain the age of Twenty-One."

The November court records of 1788 stated the Locust Children were re-indentured again: "Item 266: ordered that Martha Locus be bound unto Drury Taylor until she arrives at the age of Eighteen, aged at this time, Fourteen years, to learn the art and Mystery of carding and spinning."

Listed in that same court record is additional information on Burwell Locust. He would have been approximately nine years old at the time, and there was no listing for Isham. But, "Item 267: ordered that Isham Locust be bound unto Drury Taylor until he attains the age of twenty-one years. Now age12 years old to learn the art of Mystery Planter."

Another notation mentioning Jane Locus shows that she was deceased by 1792. The children were in the May 1792 Court Records. "Item 1127: Ordered that Burwell Locus and Mary Locus, orphans of Jane Lucas, be bound to Joshua Horn, the boy ten years the girl eight years to live with the said Joshua Horn until the boy attained 21 years and the girl 18."

Isham had a scheduled release from his indenture in 1800. He remained indentured to Drury Taylor. After his mother passed away. His contract did not transfer to Joshua Horn since Isham was sixteen years old when his mother, Jane Locust, passed away. Drury Taylor died February 13, 1839, in Nash County, North Carolina. Drury's wife, Rosamond Jincy Jackson Taylor, died in 1829.

Isham became a farmer after his twenty-one-year indentureship with the Taylor family ended. He seemed to move around quite a bit, first living in Lenoir County, North Carolina, in 1810. He lived in Robeson County in 1820 in 1830. Then Isham resided in Fayetteville, Cumberland County, in 1840 and 1850. In the 1850 Census, he lived in Cumberland County with his daughters Celia and Martha Locus Mitchell. Martha, listed as "White," was the wife of Isham Mitchell, another Revolutionary Patriot. Isham Locust appears to have passed away in 1869 in Cumberland County, North Carolina.

Isham married Margaret Roberts on August 26, 1820, in Robeson, North Carolina, the daughter of Ishmael Roberts, and was one of his fifteen children. Isham and Margaret had nine known children and Caroline Locust, their daughter. Isham and Margaret had a daughter Celia and four sons, Thomas, Edward, Watson, and Isham Locus Jr., who married Olive Evans and moved to Belmont, Ohio.

Isham's brother and Thomas' uncle, Burwell Locust, began using Pope's surname after his indenture to Lazarus Pope. Burwell Locust Pope married three times. On June 3, 1811, he married Betsey Gowen in Wake County, North Carolina and Dempsey Pope was his bondsman. He then married Lively Davis on December 24, 1833, and then he married Bethenia Scott on May 11, 1842. Phoebe Anderson lived in the home with Burwell, and so did Tempy Tyler. Still, there is no relationship mentioned for either woman.

Eli Locust was another relation of Isham's. Eli was listed in a separate court record. "Item 1128: Ordered that Eli Locus be bound to Jordan Horn, aged 12 years until he shall attain the age of twenty-one years." Jordan Horn might have been Joshua Horn's brother, the man that Burwell and Martha bound to another person at the death of their mother, Jane Locust. Nash County had a shorter indenture period than most counties. Virginia indentured Free People of Color and bound them for up to thirty-one years of age.

Virginia and North Carolina's "race-based laws required that all 'Mulattoes and Indians' be apprenticed, or bound, to a master until age 31, regardless of their mother's status. Throughout the south, they widely adopted an apprenticeship system. However, the ages of release were lowered to 21 years for males and 18 years for females during the nineteenth century in Virginia and North Carolina. Until after the Civil War, apprenticeship functioned as a system for socially and economically controlling free people of color."

Jane Locus had two brothers who fought in the Revolutionary War. Their names were Billing Locust and Arthur Locust. Both of them lived in North Carolina at the time of their Revolutionary Service. Her father was Francis Locust, and her mother was Hannah Jeffries.

Paul Heinegg notes the following record about Isham Locust's grandfather and Jane Locust's father.

Another Free Man of Color: "Francis Locus(t), born say 1728, charged Thomas and William Tabers (**Taborn**) with trespass in the 14 September 1749 Southampton County court. The suit was discontinued on the agreement of all parties [Orders 1749-54, 17].

"Francis' wife may have been a member of the **Jeffries** family since William **Sweat** and his wife, Margaret **Jeffries,** were listed together in a court record. Francis Locust and his wife Hannah, and Margaret **Jeffries**, daughter of the aforesaid Margaret. They lost their right to 190 acres on the north side of the Meherrin River in Southampton County, Virginia, in a dispute with Arthur Taylor heard at the Council of Virginia on 8 November 1753 [Hall, *Executive Journals of the Council*, V: 448]."

On 11 April 1754, Francis was one of fourteen householders sued in Southampton County by William Bynum (informer) for failing to pay the discriminatory tax on free African American and Indian women. He was found not guilty on 15 November 1754.

The court granted Bynum a new trial because his witness, Joseph Norton, did not appear. Francis was found guilty at the original trial on 13 February 1755, with Joseph Everett as Bynum's witness. The County fined Francis 1,000 pounds of tobacco, which was sufficient for concealing two tithables, so he probably had two women in his household over sixteen.

Bynum sued Francis again on 14 March 1755 on another matter, but Francis was found not guilty [Orders 1749-54, 473, 495, 507, 512, 1754-9, 23, 32, 34, 40, 69]. It appears that Francis Locust left Virginia and moved to North Carolina. He moved to avoid the discriminatory taxes that he had to pay on his wife and another female in his household.

In June 1759, he was one of Edgecombe County's freeholders, North Carolina, ordered to work on Bryant's Creek's road to the Granville line [Haun, *Edgecombe County Court Minutes*, I:238]. He received a grant for 525 acres on Turkey Creek in Nash County, North Carolina, on 9 October 1783 and a further 150 acres on the south side of the creek on 1 November 1784 [DB 3:119; 2:146].

The county taxed Francis on 800 acres, 20 cattle, and six horses in Nash County in an undated tax list, which should perhaps be 1784. He sold 300 acres of this land to Francis Anderson on 11 February 1785 [DB 1:174]. He was head of a Nash County household of eight "other free" in 1790 [NC: 70].

Francis Locust of Granville County, NC, was mentioned in an updated power of attorney to Samuel Bailey to recover his lands in Southampton County, Virginia. He proved in the February 1803 Granville County court [WB 5:291].

He sold to Jesse Hammons 250 acres on the north side of Turkey Creek on 20 November 1792 and 150 acres on the west side of the creek on 13 January 1798 [DB 6:114, 366]. This sale of land seems to coincide with the death of his daughter, Jane Locust, and in 1800 he was in Anson County, where he was head of a household of 9 "other free" (NC: 221).

The New World's discovery by European explorers gradually took the Native Americans' homelands, which caused them endless problems. Native American cultures became dramatically altered, and continuous invasions destroyed many of their ways of life. When Anglo settlers arrived in the Native American nations, Native cultures responded to pressures to adopt foreign practices, which lead to the deterioration of their own culture during the colonial period.

Native American tribes were frequently forced or tricked into giving up parts of their homeland. After the American Revolution, they faced another set of problems. The new government established policies for dealing with Native Americans. During the colonial period, Anglo settlers' insatiable desire for lands occupied by Native Americans inevitably led to the formulation of a general policy of removing unwanted inhabitants.

Political leaders, including President Thomas Jefferson, believed that the Indians should be civilized, converting them to Christianity and turning them into farmers. The transformation did not occur rapidly enough for Anglo Americans. They believed that the Native Americans were not able to assimilate into the Anglo culture. After purchasing the Louisiana territory from the French in 1803, a National policy developed to move Indians to land west of the Mississippi.

Anglos moving onto these lands pressed the United States government to do something about the Native American presence. In 1825 a formal removal policy was adopted, carried out extensively in the 1830s by President Andrew Jackson and President Martin Van Buren. The result was particularly devastating for the Native people of the southeastern United States, particularly the Cherokee, Chickasaws, Choctaws, Creeks, and Seminole. They moved hundreds of miles to new homelands.

Perhaps the most culturally devastating episode of this era concerned the removal of the Cherokee Indians. The tribes previously lived in villages in the Southern Appalachians. This area is present-day Virginia, West Virginia, Kentucky, Tennessee, western North Carolina, South Carolina, northern Georgia, and northeastern Alabama. They developed a culture based on farming, hunting, and fishing and took on some of the Anglo society's ways.

The Cherokee did not receive equal protection under the law. However, they built European-style homes on farms, laid out in European-style landscape, developed a written language, established a newspaper, and wrote a Constitution. However, they could not prevent Anglos from seizing their lands. These Native Americans, driven from their homes, were herded into internment camps and moved by force to a new ground.

President Martin Van Buren implemented this action in 1838. The U.S. Army troops under the command of Winfield Scott began rounding up Cherokees and moving them into stockades in North Carolina, Georgia, Alabama, and Tennessee. The U.S. Army also constructed additional thirty-one Forts, thirteen in Georgia, five in North Carolina, eight in Tennessee, and five in Alabama.

This relocation of the Cherokee Tribe was so tragic that the Native Americans referred to it as "The Trail of Tears." During this forced movement, some of the Cherokee arrived aboard a steamship at Sallisaw Creek's mouth near Fort Coffey, Oklahoma, on June 19, 1838. The other two groups suffered more because of severe drought and disease as they walked to Oklahoma. There was a Cherokee Indian reservation in North Carolina during the forced removal.

Almost 1,000 Cherokees escaped and hid in the rugged hills of North Carolina and became recognized as the Eastern Band of Cherokees. Approximately 8,500 of their descendants continue to occupy the Cherokee Indian reservation in Swain and Jackson counties, North Carolina. Many Locust family members lived in Oklahoma and some in Swain County, North Carolina. One of the Eastern Band of Cherokee families was the Bigmeat family, who were famous potters. Their works were very collectible, and many people sought to purchase them. Pottery was a prosperous trade for Native American women.

Native Americans did not have surnames as the Europeans did, but they took unique names. Some of the surnames they chose in addition to Locust, were: Owl, Buzzard, Sapsucker, Kingfisher, Shotpouch, Thirsty, Chunestudy, Beanstick, Soap, Fishinghawk, Fogg, Cornsilk, Chuculate, Stayathome, Duck, Frog, Mankiller, Hummingbird, Blackbird, Redbird, Squirrel, Sixkiller, Gettingdown, Big Feather, Silverheel, Sunshine, Walkingstick, Goingsnake and Bigmeat, just to name a few. Some used their Native American names, one of which was Too-noo-wee.

Some of the names listed on the Indian Census Rolls from 1885-1940 were: Mike Walkingstick, whose Cherokee name was Mi heh, and his wife, Caroline Walkingstick was Cah-too-wee-stik and their son was named James Walkingstick. Jenny Arch's name was Che-ni-yih. John Locust's Cherokee name was Or-dah-ne-Yun-duh. His wife's Cherokee name was Qualla Ann, and her American name was Polly Ann Locust. Their children were William Locust, Tiney Locust, and Peter Locust. Lacy Backwater's Cherokee name was Lacey Amah-chu-Nah, and his wife, Annie Backwater, was Ai-nih Locust.

A common belief about the Melungeons of East Tennessee was that they were an indigenous people of Appalachia existing there before the first European settlers' arrival. Genealogists working in the 20$^{th}$ century have documented a wide range of tax, court, census, and other Colonial 18$^{th}$ and 19$^{th}$ early century records. The Melungeons' ancestors migrated into the region from Virginia and Kentucky, as did their English, Scotch, Irish, Welsh, and German neighbors.

Historian Dr. Virginia Askew and genealogist Paul Heinegg and Melungeon descendant Jack Goins have traced the core Gibson and Collins families back to Louisiana County, Virginia, in the early 1700s. These families were of mixed European and African descent. The Locust family can trace their roots even further to Charles City County and Tidewater, Virginia, in the middle 1600s.

These families migrated in the first half of the 18th century from Virginia to North Carolina and South Carolina. They owned land adjacent to one another in Orange County, North Carolina. Here, they and the Bunch family were free Mulattoes subjected to bias and unfair taxable fees and tithes.

In 1755, the Melungeons were laying out frontier areas where the Free People of Color found better living conditions and could escape some of the plantation areas' racial restrictions. In 1777, the Melungeon's ancestors moved northwest to the New River Area of Virginia, where they were on the tax lists of Montgomery County.

They migrated south to Appalachia in the 1780s, and some of them moved to North Carolina, where they passed as "White" on the 1790 Census. Melungeons who resided in a part of the County were "Other Free" in 1800.

A group of these English-speaking, Christianized Indian-White and mixed-bloods lived in Halifax, North Carolina. During the time o the Revolutionary War, they maintained a village among the Catawba at the North Carolina/South Carolina border (this village was called Turkey Town).

Classified as "White" on census records with increasing frequency was a trend that continued as recently as 1935. However, some were Mulattos with straight hair. Discussing assimilation in 1994, an independent researcher characterized a gradual change of the classification of Melungeons from a Mulatto to "White" as ethnic cleansing.

Steven Pony Hill wrote an article about his Melungeon family. Hill said, "I was named after my grandmother's brother "Albert Pony Hill"...it is o.k. with me to be quoted. The only 'oral tradition' that exists in my family is that we originated from Indians. No one ever mentions our "White" ancestors (though it is apparent that we are far from full-bloods). The most plausible theory as to where the "Turk" label originated was from "Turkey Town Indians" shortened over time to "Turkey Indians" to "Turks."

The same family members who remained in Robeson, Warren, and Halifax counties of North Carolina are now known as "Lumbee" and "Haliwa-Saponi" Indians. Those of us who moved down here to Florida in 1828 are known as "Cheraw-Saponi" Indians. In 1857, several families from here (northwest Florida) joined a 'wagon train' for Louisiana. These families are now known as "Redbones." Though our white and black neighbors have labeled us all differently, we all descend from the same Indians."

Researchers have shown, and historical evidence demonstrates that the Melungeon families sought to identify as "White" as early as possible. Caroline's son, Richard D. Locust Sr., was born in 1833 and lived near Caroline and her children on the 1860 census in Lenoir County, North Carolina. Richard's wife, Esther Susan Minton Locust, and their children, Jesse, Mary Polly Ann, John Wesley, and Esther II, were listed as Mulatto on the 1860 Census.

According to the U.S. Census, Richard D. Locust lived at U.S. house number 513 in Bear Creek, Lenoir County, North Carolina. His mother, Carrie, and nephew, Thomas, were living at house number 631. Richard D. Locust was twenty-six years old at the time. His wife, Esther, was a twenty-three-year-old Mulatto female and their four children.

Richard's children were living in his home before he went to the War Between the States. His son, Jesse Locust, was born in 1854; his daughter, Mary A. Locust, was born in 1855; his son John was born in 1857; and his daughter, Esther, was born in 1859.

By the 1870 Census, the family had additional children, and all were listed as Mulatto, but Richard Sr. as "White." Richard Junior lived with his grandmother Caroline after 1870. Something very unusual occurred to the family in 1870. Richard's wife, Esther, was listed in the household with him and their children. Later that year, Esther married a man from North Carolina named Matthew "Mattie" Tilghman and moved to Tennessee. The mystery is what happened to Richard Locust. He might have died in 1870 or moved to the Cherokee land in Oklahoma. It appears that two of his children were Cherokee on the 1900 Native American Rolls.

Richard Locust Senior and Esther Carraway's son, Jesse, was born in 1854 and died in 1939. Richard Locust Junior was born in 1867 and died September 11, 1940, in Kinston, Lenoir County, North Carolina. After examination of Richard Senior and Esther's children's death certificates. It appears that their son, John Wesley "West" Locust, died in Gibson, Tennessee, at the age of 98 years old. Another of their sons, Dock Locust, also relocated to Gibson, Tennessee to be near his family and died there.

Richard Junior stated on his affidavit for Thomas Locust Fuller's pension that he traveled to Tennessee, lived there for one year from 1891 to 1892, and returned to live near Thomas later in 1892. After his grandfather, Richard Junior left the Kinston area, Peter died but returned before his grandmother, Caroline's death, in 1894.

On various census records, Esther was and as Esther Locust. Her sons listed her name as either just Esther or Easter. One of them did list her as Esther Tilghman because he knew her new married name. On each census record in Tennessee and on Kinston's 1870 census, she was "White" and on her death certificate, as well, but documented as Mulatto on the 1860 census. Richard and Esther's sons, Dock and John Wesley, also known as West Locust, were listed as African

Americans when they died in Tennessee. Their death certificates did not record their parent's names.

Paul Heinegg showed the generations that married "White" or lighter-skinned people led increasingly to European-American appearance among their descendants. Also, people who use the term "ethnic cleansing" to describe Melungeons' eventual assimilation into the Anglo community are misleading. No government or group took concerted actions against the Melungeons except for Walter Plecker. Brent Kennedy, a Melungeon himself, alleges a systematic population-wide race-based persecution of his ancestral families.

Kennedy's initial assertion is that "Melungeons were a people ravaged and nearly destroyed by the senseless excess of racism and genocide is one view of the group's disappearance. Additionally, the Melungeon families' contention was originally large landowners deprived and marginalized by Scotch, Irish, and other Northern European settlers. A shift from "Mulatto" to "White" depended on appearance and common perception of the person's life activities. Definitions of racial categories were often imprecise and ambiguous for Mulattoes or Free People of Color.

At the same time, these groups did marry each other, and there were questions about which culture took precedence. The loose terminology contributed to the disappearance of the historical records. Native Americans in the upper South, who did not live on reservations, were gradually reclassified as Mulatto or Free People of Color. Later, they were classified as having only African ancestry. As society hardened into a system that delineated persons into two races, "White" or "Negro", this racial separation condition affected some Indians of North Carolina.

Also, classification depended on the perception-based, both on the person's appearance in the community, whom he associated with, what activities involved, and whether he carried out particular obligations. A brown-complexioned Mulatto could be considered "White, " as with many brown complexioned foreigners. They moved into America, i.e., Spanish, Portuguese, and Turkish. A shift from a

"Mulatto" to "White" depended on appearance and common perception of the person's life activities.

The term "Negro" began to be associated with an entire ethnicity centered on Southern African ancestry rather than a complexion. The name tended to carry a derogatory connotation. Although Egyptians are also Africans, they were not designated as such by most Americans until recently. It took years for the general population to see that Egyptians painted themselves by their natural brown complexions in their art and monuments' walls. Since African faces are varied, individuals should be free to express pride in their ethnicity.

By designating millions of people by color instead of their heritage, the slaveholders could marginalize African ancestry. Not only did this process work to dehumanize the Africans, but it also gave the slavers an excuse to mistreat them. Captured individuals were taught to be ashamed of their heritage and were not permitted to learn to read or write. If they became literate, they might discover their true ancestry and realize that they should be free. However, there were always Africans who remembered their past. Many knew that they must revolt against a society that held them in bondage.

Though these classifications of "White" encouraged people to feel superior, they were still free to assert their pride in being European. Many stated that they were Italian, Irish, British, German, Polish, and many other ethnicities. For many years, claims of Colonial superiority permeated about ancestors who came into America very early. Not much education in the American school system concerned the early arrivals of the Melungeons' African ancestors in the Colonial Period.

People of African ancestry were not encouraged to acknowledge their family history. The families known as Melungeons in the 19th century were generally well integrated into the communities in which they lived. For example, they held property, voted, served in the Army. Some of these Free People of Color were Ishmael Roberts, Billing Locust, Thomas Locust, Benjamin Tann, and Benjamin Richardson. They were Revolutionary Soldiers from Robeson County and Halifax Counties in North Carolina.

A firm perception of race and slavery lead to the Civil War. Several Melungeon men were tried in Hawkins County for illegal voting because of the suspicion of being African. They were acquitted presumably by demonstrating to the court's satisfaction that they had no appreciable African ancestry. Like in other cases, people testifying about the men chiefly determined their fate. They said the men perceived in a community and whether they had acted "White." These acts were by voting, serving in the militia, and undertaking everyday activities.

"The law was not as involved in the recognizing of race, but in creating it." The State itself helped make people "White" in allowing men of low social status to perform "whiteness" by voting, serving on juries, and mustering into a militia. After the Civil War and during Reconstruction, Southern "whites" began to scrutinize racial identity more as they struggled to assert "white supremacy." The 1872 court assessed a person's Melungeon ancestry with relatives contending a dispute over property inheritance. This trial was in Hamilton County, Tennessee.

The court questioned the legitimacy of a marriage between a "white" man and a Melungeon woman based on the community's testimony. The court decided the woman, in this case, was not of African descent. Modern anthropological and sociological studies of Melungeon descendants produced varying results. They state that whatever their ancestry, they have become culturally indistinguishable from their non-Melungeon European neighbors.

The Melungeons shared Baptist religious affiliations and other community features. With changing attitudes and more opportunities, numerous early Melungeon pioneer families migrated from Appalachia and Robeson County, North Carolina, to other parts of the United States. Despite being culturally and linguistically identical to their European neighbors, these multicultural families are significantly different physically by complexion, hair, and facial features. These behaviors cause individuals to invite speculations as to their identity and origins.

Tennessee Melungeons, themselves, claim to be both Indian and Portuguese. Despite the scant evidence of Iberian, Spanish, Native American, and Portuguese ancestry, there may be an addition to Native American and European ethnicities. African ancestry is included, given the history of multi-racial families.

The social problems associated with race and many southern families with multi-ethnic ancestry claim Portuguese or American Indians, specifically Cherokee ancestry, to deny African ancestry. The 1956 law passed by Congress also recognizes the Lumbees as Indians.

# CHAPTER 10

## Are Croatan Indians Lumbee?

Thomas heard of his Free Person of Color and Melungeon status from his grandfather, Isham Locust. The latter told him of his family's situation and ancestry before 1860.

The terms "Free Person of Color" or "Melungeon" was not accurate after 1865 because every person of color was legally "free" in America after the civil war ended. Being "Legally Free" was the law, but "Planters" held many thousands of African descendants in slavery, agricultural bondage, prison, and industrial peonage as late as the 1920s.

The term "Melungeon" (by the documentation of some historians) originated in Angola, Africa. It was a derivative of an Angolan word, Malanga. Tim Hashaw, an expert on Melungeon ancestry, and other historians have published books and articles dealing with Melungeon's definition and their family origins.

These experts explained the Melungeons are descendants of the Africans who arrived in the colonies as early as 1619. A Spanish slave ship brought the Angolans to Colonial Virginia from a West Central African colony. Their original destination was Vera Cruz, New Spain, which is present-day Mexico. The Portuguese captured about 350 Africans and enslaved them for a contract with a slave dealer in Seville. The ship arrived in James City, Virginia, on August 23, 1619.

The history of the early Africans who lived in Tidewater, Virginia, had much to do with the Melungeon people's beginnings. Since they married or had children with Europeans and Native Americans beginning early in the 1600s, they developed a family sense. These families' descendants moved to other areas of Virginia and eventually moved to North Carolina.

Since 1790, Native Americans in the southern states were enumerated as "Free Persons of Color" on the local and federal censuses, included with African Americans. By 1835, in the wake of

Nat Turner's Slave Rebellion of 1831, North Carolina, like other southern states, reduced the rights of Free People of Color, including those identifying as Native Americans. The legislature withdrew their rights to vote, serve on juries, own and use firearms, and learn to read and write because they feared that they would aid slave rebellions.

During the 1830s, the federal government forced Indian Removal, relocating the Cherokee and others of the Five Civilized Tribes to Indian Territory west of the Mississippi River. Native Americans who stayed in the Southeast tended to live in frontier and marginal areas to avoid Anglo supervision. Free People of Color moved into the backcountry and married into one another's families, then became known as Melungeon, but some did not like the term.

Some people did not want a classification of "Melungeon." It was a name given to people in Robeson County, North Carolina, who were members of (what some called) "a tri-racial isolate." This group of people lived in the southeastern United States, mainly in the Cumberland Gap area and central Appalachia. This area included portions of East Tennessee, southwest Virginia, and North Carolina.

DNA proves that Melungeons' descendants have a mix of European, Sub-Saharan African, and Native American ancestry. Although there is no consensus on how many such groups exist, the estimates are as high as two hundred separate groups. Some self-identifying Melungeons disliked the term "tri-racial" because they believed it was pejorative.

In the Twentieth Century, some people considered the term of Melungeon to be offensive. DNA testing of the descendants is limited, but the Melungeon DNA project has had more public results so far. It shows the overwhelming European and Sub-Saharan African heritage of males in several families traditionally as a DNA dump identified as Melungeon.

This finding is consistent with the documented work by genealogists Paul Heinegg and Dr. Virginia D. Morris. They use various historical records to show the formation of Colonial families.

The families were ancestors to Free People of Color in the Nineteenth Century.

Caroline Locust, Thomas's mother, is presumed to be Margaret Roberts Locust and Isham Locust's daughter. Caroline has an assumed relationship with Isham Locust, determined by both age and proximity. It is sometimes difficult to prove the exact relationship of these Melungeon families before the 1880 Census. There are varying opinions of and wide variations in descriptions dealing with each ancestor. There is also a lack of clear consensus on who is designated and included under the term Melungeon.

Almost every author on this subject gives a slightly different list of Melungeon-associated surnames. Still, the British surnames Collins and Gibson appear most frequently, and genealogist Pat Elder calls them core surnames. The Locust family is on the Cherokee rolls, and some members list as Mulattoes and Melungeon.

Many researchers also include Bunch, Goins, Goodman, Heard, Minor, and several other surnames. However, not all families with these surnames are Melungeon. Some families are considered different ethnic backgrounds or the lines are different, and we should examine them individually. Ultimately, the answer to the question, who is Melungeon, depends primarily on which families are under that designation.

The original meaning of the word Melungeon is obscure from the Mid-Nineteenth to the Twentieth century. It recurred exclusively to one "tri-ethnic isolate group." The ancestral identity of the Melungeon is still a highly controversial subject. There is a complete disagreement among secondary sources regarding ethnic, linguistic, cultural, and geographical origins. Melungeons can clarify their identity as families of diverse origins who migrated together and intermarried with each other.

Most modern-day descendants of Appalachian families traditionally regarded as Melungeon are generally of Anglo appearance. Often, though not always, with dark hair and eyes and an olive complexion. The Melungeon's descriptions vary widely from observer to observer, from Middle Eastern to Native American to light-complexioned African American.

The Roanoke Indians are said to have been from North Carolina. Their descendants in Robeson County are known as the Lumbee Indians. There is some controversy about the Lumbee's origin as they excluded them from the Five Civilized Tribes.

On June 30, 1914, O.M. McPherson published the following "A Report on the Condition and Tribal Rights of the Indians of Robeson and Adjoining Counties of North Carolina" excerpts below:

"The Croatan Indians comprise a body of mixed-blood people residing chiefly in Robeson County, North Carolina. A few people reside in Bladen, Columbus, Cumberland, Scotland, and Hoke Counties in North Carolina and Sumter, Marlboro, and Dillon Counties in South Carolina. "They further have had a tradition among them that their ancestors, or some of them, came from "Roanoke in Virginia."

An excerpt was taken from a letter by Hamilton McMillan of Fayetteville, North Carolina, dated July 17, 1890. The letter read: "The Croatan tribe lives principally in Robeson County, North. There are quite a number of them settled in counties adjoining in North and South Carolina. In Sumter County, South Carolina, there is a branch of the tribe and East Tennessee. Whereas, the Indians now living in Robeson County claim to be descendants of a friendly tribe who once resided in eastern North Carolina on the Roanoke River."

The Croatans, known as "Redbones," had a street in Fayetteville named after them because some once lived on it. Known by this name in Sumter County, South Carolina, they are quiet and peaceable and have a church of their own. Neighbors said: "they are proud and high-spirited, and caste is powerful among them."

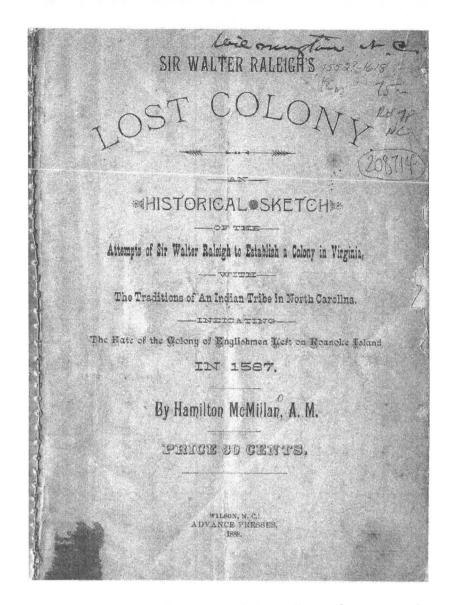

SIR WALTER RALEIGH'S

# LOST COLONY

— AN —

## HISTORICAL SKETCH

— OF THE —

Attempts of Sir Walter Raleigh to Establish a Colony in Virginia,

— WITH —

The Traditions of An Indian Tribe in North Carolina.

— INDICATING —

The Fate of the Colony of Englishmen Left on Roanoke Island

IN 1587.

By Hamilton McMillan, A. M.

PRICE 30 CENTS.

WILSON, N. C.:
ADVANCE PRESSES,
1888.

This statement stands as one of the earliest references to the mixed-blood settlement in Sumter County. McMillan presented himself as a person well acquainted with the Sumter County, South Carolina people. He proposed them to be Indians and closely related to the present-day Lumbee.

The Lumbee have been in North Carolina since very early on. The Cherokee and other tribes were taken to the available Indian land and forced to live on Reservations. The Lumbee are a combination of the Cherokee, Catawba, and other Sioux tribes. They, as smaller tribes,

151

were moved and pushed out of their territories. They began banding together to protect themselves from the encroachment of Europeans. Native Americans realized that their land could, by past evidence, and the Europeans would send further into the woods.

Lumbees were called Croatan Indians. In 1885, North Carolina passed a law sponsored by Hamilton McMillan, a Democrat from Robeson County, creating separate school districts for the former Free Persons of Color of the county. McMillan invented the name "Crow" for these Indians and theorized that they had descended from a friendly tribe of Indians on the Roanoke River in eastern North Carolina.

This North Carolina Bill changed the history of Indians in the Southeast. Anthropologist James Moni included the Croatan Indians and other mixed-race communities in adjoining North and South Carolina counties in his Indian tribes' studies. He traveled throughout the Southeastern States to discover the lost tribes.

Person County granted a group called "All Issue Negroes" their separate school on February 2, 1887. The county discontinued this school about 1890. January 19th, another school was "Mongolian" through 1906, "Cuban" from 6 April 1988 to 1911, and listed for the Indian race in 1912. All other Melungeon North Carolina Indian tribes followed the Sampson County - Coharie Indians, Columbus County – Waccamaw- Siouan Indians, and Halifax County - Haliwa-Saponi Indians. Virginia recognized the former Free Person of Color Community in Norfolk County as Nansemond Indians and Amherst County as Monacan Indians.

Anglo people shortened the name to the pejorative "Crows." Their name then changed to Cherokee Indians of Robeson County in 1913. The name was changed again to Siouan Indians of the Lumber River from 1934 to 1935. The U.S. Congress recognized them as Lumbee Indians in 1956. But while North Carolina has long recognized the tribe, the federal government had denied the Lumbee that status since 1956. Congress denied members full legal status and the corresponding access to benefits.

Vice President Joseph Biden addressed the Lumbee tribe in September 2020 in a statement from his campaign. He stated that "Six decades ago, Congress recognized the Lumbee Tribe but denied it the benefits that all other federally recognized tribes receive. It is past time for the federal government to rectify this injustice and fully recognize the Lumbee tribe, providing it with the critical resources it needs to prosper."

Situated mainly around Robeson, Scotland, and Hoke counties, the Lumbee make up the most prominent American Indian tribe east of the Mississippi River. Its 55,000 members hold annual powwows to display their Native American traditions. The tribe keeps its office inside a turtle-shaped building in Pembroke in Robeson County.

The Lumbee began to dislike the Melungeon name because of the negative connotation. They began to use Lumbee Indians because they were living near the Lumber River. Before World War II, a sure way to get a black eye was to go to Sumter County, South Carolina, and call someone a "Turk" or go to Tennessee and call someone a "Melungeon."

"The "Croatoan" Indians killed General Howe while he was crabbing. When John White and the English expedition returned, he made this remark: "we passed toward the place where they were left in sundry houses, but we found the houses taken downe, and the place very strongly enclosed with a high palisado of great trees, with cortynes (curtains) and flankers very Fort-like."

Moreover, one of the chiefe trees or postes at the right side of the entrance had the barke taken off, and 5 foote from the ground in faire Capitall letters was graven CROATOAN without any crosse or Signe of distresse; this done, we entred into the palisado, where we found many Barres of Iron, two pigges of Lead, foure iron fowlers, Iron Sacker-shotte and such like heavie things, throwen here and there, almost overgrowen with grasse and weedes."

Thomas wanted to know if the Lumbee Indians were the descendants of the Croatan Indians. They had changed their name to the Lumbee because of the Lumber River. He stated that his grandfather told him the story of William Lucas.

William Lucas was listed on the ship's rolls and was a member of the Lost Colony Immigrants. Roberta Estes, a genealogist, developed a goal to discover the fate of the Roanoke Lost Colonists. She stated, "In 1587, Sir Walter Raleigh financed a venture in which 116 men, women, and children were planning to establish the first permanent colony in the New World. Their goal was to raise tobacco and other supplies that colonists could not obtain in England and search for precious minerals, like gold and silver, and find food sources.

In the fall of 1587, the colonists finally arrived on Roanoke Island in present-day North Carolina; after an arduous journey, their food supplies became ruined. They sent John White, whom they had elected governor, back to England to obtain food and supplies and expected his return in the spring of 1588. However, the Spanish attacked England, having no Navy, pressed all of her fishing vessels and private merchant ships into naval service.

In 1590, three years after leaving the colonists, including his daughter, son-in-law, and infant granddaughter, John White returned to Roanoke Island. He found it deserted but not destroyed. It appeared as if the colonists had simply moved. A single word, a clue, Croatoan, was carved on a tree.

Croatoans were friendly Indians living nearby. Before John's departure, he had instructed the colonists to carve crosses if they had to leave in distress. There were no crosses. John White would spend the rest of his life searching for the Lost Colonists. Many hints and clues indicate that some of the Colonists survived and assimilated into the native tribes. Who and where are they today?

In 1993, the original site of the Croatoan village was located. Subsequent archaeological and genealogical research suggests that the colonists did survive. When the land was granted to settlers, it was given to some of those survivors who were considered Indians.

With recent advances in DNA for genealogy, we finally have, today, the ability to solve the mystery. We have created a plan that combines history, genealogy, and DNA to solve the mystery.

Many who left the state were enumerated in the 1840-1860 censuses of Indiana, Illinois, Ohio, and Michigan. Some went to Canada and a few to Haiti and Liberia. By 1857 when Henry Chavers (Chavis) immigrated to Liberia, life for free African Americans in North Carolina must have been genuinely oppressive. A letter written for him to his friend, Dr. Ellis Malone of Lewisburg in Franklin County, describing Liberia sounds like that of a recently liberated slave:

*"This Land of Freedom ... a nation of free and happy Children of a hitherto downcast and oppressed Race ... I now begin to enjoy life as a man should do ... did my Coloured Friends only know or could they have seen what I already have seen they would not hesitate a moment to come to this Glorious Country."*

By 1870, many of those who remained behind were living in virtually the same condition as the freed slaves. In the 1870 census for Northampton County, North Carolina, the most common occupation listed for those who were free before 1800 was "farm laborer," the same work as the former slaves. Some Melungeons married former slaves, like Thomas's mother, Caroline Locust. His father, Peter Fuller, was enslaved and lived next door to Caroline. They could not legally marry until 1865. By the Twentieth Century, these Free People of Color had no idea their ancestors had been "free."

Isham Locust, Caroline's father, was "Free Born" in 1776 and lived in Nash County, North Carolina, when he was a young child and was indentured. His mother, Jane Locust, died in 1792 when he was only 16 years old. It is unsure if he was allowed to spend time with his mother while indentured. However, it is known that he was not free to leave his indenture before he reached the age of twenty-one years.

*Poster Art: Fort Macon State Park.*
*Poster Photographed by S. R. 2013*

Isham served in the War of 1812 and was a Lumbee Indian. He married Margaret Roberts in 1820 at the age of 44 years old. He moved around as a Waterman, living in Lenoir, Fayetteville, Cumberland, and Robeson Counties in North Carolina. Margaret's father, Ishmael Roberts, was a Revolutionary Patriot who was also Lumbee Indian. Margaret's mother, Silvia "Silvey" Archer, was a Cherokee Indian.

Isham's mother, Jane Locus, was born in 1757, and his grandfather, Francis Locus, was born in Virginia in 1728. Francis was the son of a Mulatto woman whose identity is unknown. Descended two generations from Elizabeth Lucas and John Kecotan's child

156

(maybe John Locust) was born in 1665 in Charles City County, Virginia. The church threatened Elizabeth Lucas with 30 lashes for having him out of wedlock.

Thomas Locust Fuller descended from Elizabeth Lucas and John Kecotan. Elizabeth Lucas was born in England and was an indentured servant maid to Rice Hooe Sr. Her child was born on his property. Her child was bound at her death and was born "Free" in the Virginia Colony. John Kecotan, a Free Person of Color, and Elizabeth Lucas's conditions affected their descendants' freedom.

Thomas did not understand everything that his grandfather, Isham, told him about his family. He did not understand why his grandfather, IshamLocust, Uncle Burwell Locust Pope, and Aunt Martha Sallie Locust were taken away from their mother. Nor why they were indentured to men who did not care for them. Thomas later discovered that they were first indentured to his great uncle, Lazarus Pope.

There were many things that Thomas did not understand because he did not see his family as different. He believed that they did not deserve mistreatment in this way since they were kind and hardworking people. Thomas did not understand why his military comrades were enslaved or why so many of them had to die so that his people could be free.

But Thomas did understand that his family, always designated as "Free." Though they suffered many indignities, they escaped the tragedy of being enslaved. He now knew their history and knew that his family were most certainly Melungeon and Free.

157

# Sources

Abercrombie, Janice Luck. *Louisa County, Virginia Judgments 1766-1790: Compiled from the Microfilm of the Judgment / Loose Papers of the Louisa County Clerk's Office*. Athens, GA: Iberian Publishing Company, 1998.

Albion University. *Catalogue of Albion Academy Normal and Industrial School, Franklinton, Franklin County, NC for Academic Year 1901-1902*. Raleigh, NC: Edwards and Broughton, 1902.

Berlin, Ira. *Slaves without Masters: The Free Negro in the Antebellum South*. New York: Pantheon Books, 1974.

Blu, Karen I. *The Lumbee Problem: The Making of an American Indian People*. Lincoln, NB: University of Nebraska Press, 2001.

Certificate No. 113, 1968, Thomas Fuller (Alias) Thomas Lucas, Private, Company L, 14th USCT North Carolina Heavy Artillery, Case Files of Approved Pension Applications of Veterans Who Served in the Army and Navy. Mainly in the Civil War and the War with Spain ("Civil War and Later Survivors' Certificates"), 1861–1934; Civil War and Later Pension Files; Records of the Department of Veterans Affairs, Record Group 15; National Archives Building, Washington, DC.

Clinton, Catherine. *The Black Soldier 1492 to the Present*. Boston: Houghton Mifflin Company, 2000.

Dial, Adolph L. *Indians of North America: The Lumbee*. New York: Chelsea House Publishers, 1993.

Foley, Louise Pledge Heath. *Early Virginia Families Along the James River, Minutes of the Council, pp. 21 and 30*. Virginia Historical Society.

Franklin, John Hope. *The Free Negro in North Carolina, 1790-1860*. Chapel Hill, NC: University of NC Press, 1995.

Gehman, Mary. *The Free People of Color of New Orleans: An Introduction* (5th Ed.). Chelsea, MI: Sheridan Books, 2009.

Hashaw, Tim. *Children of Perdition: Melungeons and the Struggle for Mixed America*. Macon, Georgia: Mercer Univ. Press, 2006.

Heinegg, P. *Free African Americans of North Carolina, Virginia, and South Carolina* (5th Ed.). Baltimore: Clearfield, 2005.

Hollandsworth, James G. Jr., *The Louisiana Native Guards: The Black Military Experience during the Civil War.* Baton Rouge, LA: Louisiana State University Press, 1995.

Hume, Ivor Noel. *The Virginia Adventure: Roanoke to James Towne, an Archaeological and Historical Odyssey.* New York: Alfred A. Knopf, Inc., 1994.

Holley, Joseph Winthrop, et al. *The Lincoln University Class Book Senior Class of 1900.* Pennsylvania: Lincoln University Publisher, 1900.

Morgan, Edmund S. *American Slavery, American Freedom: The Ordeal in Colonial Virginia.* New York: W. W. Norton and Company, 1975.

Robbins, Coy D. *Forgotten Hoosiers: African Heritage in Orange County, Indiana.* Westminster, MD: Heritage Books, 2011.

Taylor, Charles A. *Juneteenth: A Celebration of Freedom.* Madison, WI: Praxis Publication Inc., 1995.

United States Department of the Interior: *Trail of Tears: National Historic Trail Draft Comprehensive Management and Use Plan and Environmental Assessment.* Denver: National Park Service, 1991.

Vincent, Stephen A. *Southern Seed Northern Soil: African-American Farm Communities in the Midwest, 1765-1900.* Bloomington, IN: Indiana Univ. Press, 1999.

Wesley, Charles H., and Patricia W. Romero. *Negro Americans in the Civil War: From Slavery to Citizenship.* New York: Publishers Company, Inc., 1967-8.

White, Deborah Gray. *Let My People Go: African Americans 1804-1860.* New York: Oxford University Press, 1996.

WPA Writers Project comps. *The Negro in Virginia.* Winston Salem, NC: John F. Blair Publisher, 1994.

# ABOUT THE AUTHOR

Gigi is a Historian (Phi Alpha Theta), Genealogist, Virginia Humanities Scholar, Award-Winning Author of "Thomas the Melungeon: Volume 1 and Thomas the Melungeon: Vol 2: Walking in His Footsteps from Angola to Jamestown," Poet, Speaker, Owner, and Curator of Best Richardson African Diaspora Literature and Culture Nonprofit Museum. She studied her M.A. in Literature at Morgan State University and an Undergraduate in African American History and Journalism. The Order First Families of N.C. confirm her proven DNA and hereditary lineage; Daughters American Revolution; Daughters Union Veterans of Civil War; Vice President-Sons & Daughters U.S. Middle Passage; Daughters of Founders and Patriots of America; Colonial Dames 17th Century; Colonial Dames of America; Past Florida Governor-Sons & Daughters of Pilgrims; Society of New England Women; Afro American Historical & Genealogical Society and Midwest African American Genealogy Institute. Gigi teaches genealogy and has proven her "Best" and associated European American ancestors born in 1583 and her "Locust, Kecotan, Cornish, Sweat, and Jefferies" FPOC ancestors 1610. Gigi was born in Goldsboro, NC, raised in Camden, NJ., and now resides in Tampa, FL, with her husband and lived and worked in Turkey, Korea, and Germany.

*www.bradlcmuseum.com*

*Instagram: @GigiBestII*

*Twitter: @GigiBest18*

*To inquire about booking Gigi Best for*

*a speaking engagement, please contact*

*BBRT Associates LLC at*

*bradlcmuseum@gmail.com*

Made in the USA
Columbia, SC
18 September 2023

22983714R00089